Report Number 60
Group for the
Advancement of Psychiatry

Sex and the College Student

A Developmental Perspective
on Sexual Issues on the Campus;
Some Guidelines for Administrative
Policy and Understanding of Sexual Issues

Formulated by the
Committee on the College Student

Volume VI*, Report Number 60, November, 1965

INTRODUCTION 9

1. THE DEVELOPMENT AND INTEGRATION OF
   SEXUALITY IN THE PERSONALITY 18
   Sexual Development in Childhood 18
   Sexual Development in Adolescence 20
   The Search for Identity 26
   The Relationship Between Sexual and
      Intellectual Development 29
   The Relationship Between Adolescence and
      the Adult World 34

2. SEXUAL ISSUES ON THE CAMPUS 38
   Heterosexual Behavior 38
   Contraception, Pregnancy, and Abortion 43
   Homosexual Behavior 55
   Sexual Deviations 64
   Silent Problems 66
   Faculty-Student Relationships 71
   Sex Education 77

*This report is the first in a series of Reports and Symposiums that will comprise Volume VI. For a list of other GAP publications on topics related to the subject of this report, please see inside back cover.

3. COLLEGE POLICY, CAMPUS REGULATIONS,
   AND SEXUAL CONDUCT 80
   Campus Regulations 80
   Comparison of Two Educational Institutions 87
   Administrative Attitudes Toward Individual
   Cases 92

4. GUIDELINES FOR COLLEGE POLICY TOWARD
   SEXUALITY 98

APPENDIX A: PSYCHOSEXUAL DEVELOPMENT FROM
INFANCY THROUGH ADOLESCENCE 115
   The Infantile Period 116
   The Oedipal Period 118
   The Latency Period 119
   Prepuberty 120
   Adolescence 120

APPENDIX B: SELECTED READINGS 124

STATEMENT OF PURPOSE

The GROUP FOR THE ADVANCEMENT OF PSYCHIATRY has a membership of approximately 185 psychiatrists, organized in the form of a number of working committees which direct their efforts toward the study of various aspects of psychiatry and toward the application of this knowledge to the fields of mental health and human relations.

Collaboration with specialists in other disciplines has been and is one of GAP's working principles. Since the formation of GAP in 1946 its members have worked closely with such other specialists as anthropologists, biologists, economists, statisticians, educators, lawyers, nurses, psychologists, sociologists, social workers, and experts in mass communication, philosophy, and semantics. GAP envisages a continuing program of work according to the following aims:

1. To collect and appraise significant data in the field of psychiatry, mental health, and human relations;
2. To re-evaluate old concepts and to develop and test new ones;
3. To apply the knowledge thus obtained for the promotion of mental health in good human relations.

GAP is an independent group and its reports represent the composite findings and opinions of its members only, guided by its many consultants.

SEX AND THE COLLEGE STUDENT *was formulated by the Committee on the College Student.* The members of this Committee as well as all other Committees are listed below.*

---

* The Committee is deeply indebted to the following consultants, who participated in the discussions, accumulation of data, and the report's formation: Professor Joseph Katz, Research Director, Student Development Study, Institute for the Study of Human Problems, Stanford University; Ernst Prelinger, Ph.D., Clinical Psychologist, Department of University Health, Yale University; and Professor John T. Rule (formerly Dean of Students), Massachusetts Institute of Technology.

The Committee is also indebted to Leonard Stein, M.D., Department of Psychiatry, University of Wisconsin Medical School, who contributed to the early draft of the report.

For their services in preparation of the manuscript, the Committee expresses its thanks to Marilyn Hainesworth and Jacqueline Tarrer.

Acknowledgment is also made of an anonymous enabling gift to defray editorial expenses.

Louis C. English, Pomona, N.Y.
Robert L. Leopold, Philadelphia
John A. P. Millet, New York
Florence Powdermaker, Ridgefield, Conn.
Bertram Schaffner, New York
Bryant M. Wedge, Princeton, N.J.

COMMITTEE ON MEDICAL EDUCATION
Roy M. Whitman, Cincinnati, Chr.
Hugh T. Carmichael, Chicago
Robert S. Daniels, Chicago
Saul Harrison, Ann Arbor
David Hawkins, Chapel Hill
Herbert C. Modlin, Topeka
William L. Peltz, Philadelphia
David S. Sanders, New York
Elvin V. Semrad, Boston

COMMITTEE ON
MENTAL RETARDATION
Leo Madow, Philadelphia, Chr.
Howard V. Bair, Parsons, Kans.
Peter W. Bowman, Pownal, Me.
Stuart M. Finch, Ann Arbor
George Tarjan, Pomona, Calif.
Warren T. Vaughan, Jr., San Mateo
Thomas G. Webster, Bethesda
Cecil L. Wittson, Omaha
Henry H. Work, Los Angeles

COMMITTEE ON
PREVENTIVE PSYCHIATRY
Leonard J. Duhl, Bethesda, Chr.
Gerald Caplan, Boston
Jules V. Coleman, New Haven
Stephen Fleck, New Haven
Albert J. Glass, Oklahoma City
Benjamin Jeffries, Harper Woods, Mich.
Mary E. Mercer, Nyack, N.Y.
Marvin E. Perkins, New York
Harold M. Visotsky, Chicago
Stanley F. Yolles, Bethesda

COMMITTEE ON
PSYCHIATRY IN INDUSTRY
Spencer Bayles, Houston, Chr.
Matthew Brody, Brooklyn

Alan A. McLean, New York
Kenneth J. Munden, Memphis
Graham C. Taylor, Montreal
Harry H. Wagenham, Philadelphia

COMMITTEE ON PSYCHIATRY AND LAW
Gene L. Usdin, New Orleans, Chr.
Edward T. Auer, St. Louis
John Donnelly, Hartford
Jay Katz, New Haven
Zigmond M. Lebensohn, Washington
Andrew S. Watson, Ann Arbor

COMMITTEE ON
PSYCHIATRY AND RELIGION
Mortimer Ostow, New York, Chr.
Sidney Furst, New York
John W. Higgins, St. Louis
Stanley A. Leavy, New Haven
Earl A. Loomis, Jr., New York
Albert J. Lubin, Woodside, Calif.

COMMITTEE ON
PSYCHIATRY AND SOCIAL WORK
Edward C. Frank, Louisville, Chr.
C. Knight Aldrich, Chicago
Maurice R. Friend, New York
John MacLeod, Cincinnati
John Nemiah, Boston
Eleanor A. Steele, Denver
Edward M. Weinshel, San Francisco

COMMITTEE ON PSYCHOPATHOLOGY
Marvin Stein, New York, Chr.
Wagner H. Bridger, New York
Neil Burch, Houston
James H. Ewing, Media, Pa.
Daniel X. Freedman, New Haven
Milton Greenblatt, Boston
Paul E. Huston, Iowa City
P. Herbert Leiderman, Palo Alto, Calif.
George Ruff, Philadelphia
Charles Shagass, Iowa City
Albert J. Silverman, New Brunswick, N.J.

INTRODUCTION

Background

In November 1963 the Dean of Harvard College wrote to the *Harvard Crimson,* in defense of the administration's decision to review college rules permitting boys to entertain girls in their rooms during specified hours:

> We have been badly shaken up recently by some severe violations of our rules of decent standards of behavior . . . Trouble has arisen because what was once considered a pleasant privilege has now for a growing number of students come to be considered a license to use the college rooms for wild parties or for sexual intercourse.

The Dean also told newsmen, "We are even more concerned with attitudes than we are with incidents." What disturbed him most, he said, was the students' belief that a student's behavior in his room was of no concern to the college, that a student's room was his castle and his sexual behavior his private affair.

At about the same time from the London press came reports of two scandals at Oxford University, involving the presence of a girl in a boy's room—an offense for which students have traditionally been expelled. The students then staged a "revolution" to demonstrate their conviction that their sexual behavior should be of no concern to the college authorities. The students stated bluntly, "We come here to learn, we don't come here to have our sexual life regulated."

In contrast is a recent statement from the Assistant Dean of Columbia University in New York:

> Too often students are led to feel sexuality is acceptable as animal passion, love, or anything in between . . . Institutions . . . have been remiss in their responsibility to show the 15-, 16-, 17-, and 18-year olds entrusted to them how to make responsible judgments—on an individual basis—about sex.

The controversies at Harvard and Oxford and the statement from Columbia demonstrate an important fact in contemporary life.

Standards of sexual conduct and sexual morality are rapidly changing. While the phenomenon frequently described as a sexual revolution cannot be documented, it is clear that college students are asserting with increasing militancy their right to privacy and self-determination in matters pertaining to their own sexual activity. Authorities differ as to the extent of premarital sexual intercourse among students, but there is consensus that the double standard increasingly is being discarded and that college girls more often seek sexual experience during the college years than their mothers did. Reports that college youth are uniformly promiscuous and amoral seem as wide of the mark as insistence that there has been no change at all in the sexual behavior of the young. There is evidence of earlier biological maturation in adolescence, of a widespread pattern of going steady, and of more open and vocal discussion of sexual matters. College students are often well-informed (although gross misinformation and utter lack of knowledge persist) about current methods of birth control and the hazards of illegal abortions, not to mention their acquaintance with the plethora of present-day literature on sexual behavior.

Traditional external controls over sexual behavior have been modified by recent scientific advances and cultural changes. These range from the broad impact of psychoanalytic theory, the findings of the Kinsey report, availability of information about birth control, increasing ease of use of contraceptives, and effective treatment of venereal disease to the modification of parental authority in relation to teen-agers and the less pervasive authority of religion. At the same time, there is increased emphasis on the emotional meaning of relationships and on going steady, possibly reflecting a new student morality. In seeking guidance, the students find ample evidence not only that the adult world lacks consensus on acceptable standards of sexual behavior but that the underlying values of human relationships are murky as well. Young people are quick to perceive the inadequacy of "Do as we say, not as we do." Discussion of these matters is no longer restricted to the privacy of the family, the physician's office, or the dean's office; sex has become an accepted subject for the public forum on the campus as elsewhere. The continuing and periodically intense campus dialogue suggests that young people are both testing authority and searching for guidelines. While students often appear simply to be asserting independence, some may also be seeking new soundings and limits in an area where the existing charts handed down by the older generation seem to many young people to be out of date and where adult attitudes frequently appear to be based on conflicting values, lack of candor, and failure to respond to new realities.

The Harvard experience and, by implication, the situation at Columbia demonstrate the wide gap between rules and regulations apparently (but not explicitly) designed to inhibit sexuality on campus and the insistent reality of student behavior. Two examples serve to illustrate student reaction.

In one college, visits of girls in men's dormitory rooms are permitted at specified hours if the door remains open "a book's width." Inventive students have reduced the regulation to its ultimate absurdity by wedging match books between door and door jamb. Parents of students in a co-educational college were as shocked as college officials some time ago to receive an issue of the campus newspaper with banner headlines proclaiming "Seven Safe Ways to Do It." A well-known gynecologist had visited the college and had made a forthright talk on contraceptive techniques. Despite official alarm, the offending issue of the newspaper is still regarded by students as a most valuable and realistic document on sex.

The issue posed is the extent to which the colleges come to grips *explicitly* with sexual behavior. Students are aware of the intent of rules about closed doors and are uninhibited in announcing their concerns in the campus press. As Erikson has suggested, it may be not that young people have changed, but rather that the process of change itself has changed. Confronted with a new and untested situation, young men and women seek to establish values and meaning—just as they always have. Honesty and candor assume special significance under these circumstances, and adolescents can be counted upon to test authority until they are forthcoming.

What is normal? What is healthy? What is right? What is moral? What rules should be made? What penalties enforced? Should sexual activity be a totally private concern? What about homosexuality on the campus? Should the college stand *in loco parentis?* What should be the official attitude toward the unmarried pregnant student?

These are only some of the complex, urgent, and sometimes painful questions confronting presidents, deans, and students, not to mention parents and faculty. It is not surprising that these questions are addressed with increasing frequency to psychiatrists whose discipline includes specific knowledge about human development and insight into the dynamics of the young adult's sexuality. The Committee on the College Student of the Group for the Advancement of Psychiatry therefore undertook to prepare this report on problems of sex in late adolescence and young adulthood, particularly as these relate to the college experience.

Although it might sometimes seem desirable to resolve the foregoing questions by means of moral judgment and a clear-cut set of rules and regulations, it is the Committee's conviction that psychoanalytic theory and clinical experience can be most useful by furthering understanding of the dynamics of sexual behavior among college students. We hope that to the extent the present report succeeds in this purpose, a broader basis may be established for the attitudes and policies toward sexual behavior that will inevitably be evolved by educators and students in this time of changing mores.

Purposes of the Report

The report is addressed primarily to deans and other college officers; it should also interest psychiatrists and other counselors who work with college students, parents, teachers, and students themselves. It has four major purposes:

1. to describe some sexual aspects of individual development and to relate these to issues of sexual behavior on the campus;
2. to discuss dynamics of sexual behavior among college students;
3. to explore the relationship between official college policies and student behavior;
4. to suggest guidelines, both theoretical and practical, for understanding and formulating policy toward student sexual behavior in the college setting.

Method

The report draws on the pooled clinical and administrative experience of a group of nine psychiatrists and three consultants, (a dean, a faculty member, and a clinical psychologist) who have worked with students over the past 20 years in college health services, in private practice, or in research. They represent colleges and universities of varying sizes, in urban and exurban settings, from the East, Midwest, and West. We have drawn from relevant confidential material rarely available at the administrative level. The report brings to bear the particular perspective of the psychoanalytically oriented psychiatrist who has a medical responsibility for students, but who also acts as consultant in matters of administrative or educational policy.

Material was gathered from four main sources. First, members of the Committee interviewed deans and counselors on selected campuses to learn at first hand the current attitudes of college officials toward sexual behavior and to look into actual practices in handling situations involving sexual issues. Second, 49 institutions were asked for materials that might shed light on prevailing standards and regulations affecting student sexuality: statements, printed rules, handbooks, and so forth. The Committee reviewed materials submitted by a representative sampling of 37 institutions. Third, the Committee surveyed some of the relevant literature in the field and prepared the selected readings appended to the report. Finally, Committee members contributed for discussion individual case histories drawn from their own clinical and research experience.

Organization

Certain matters treated in the report are likely to be of greater interest than others to some readers. Although the report is designed as a whole, individual sections have been organized to take into account the possibility that some readers may wish to read selectively.

Part I of the report describes the development and integration of sexuality in the personality, stressing in particular the developmental tasks of late adolescence and the interrelated aspects of sexuality and intellectual development. We recognize that many of our readers may already be informed in this area. However, the psychoanalytic concept of the development of the human personality is, in the opinion of this Committee, central to the understanding of sexual behavior; this discussion has therefore been included.

Part II, "Sexual Issues on the Campus," describes and discusses from a developmental point of view types of sexual activity encountered on the campus and some of the issues they raise for college authorities. Topics include heterosexual and homosexual behavior, contraception, pregnancy and abortion, deviations, and faculty-student relationships. Part II ends with a brief comment on sex education at the college level.

In Part III, we report on current official college attitudes and regulations, compare the attitudes of two institutions, and discuss administrative action in a specific case.

The last section of the report suggests some guidelines for understanding and handling sexual issues on the campus. It suggests points of view that our experience and this study lead us to believe should be considered in the making of college policy. It also suggests practical procedures that we believe to be appropriate and realistically related to the needs of the institution and its students. The Guidelines should be read and considered in the context of the whole report.

An appendix has been included for those readers who are interested in a brief description of the psychoanalytic approach to the dynamics of sexual development.

Underlying Assumptions

The report reflects throughout certain concepts and values about which the Committee members are in agreement:

1. In common usage, sex refers to the drive originating at puberty toward genital union between men and women with the biological purpose of procreation. The emphasis is on physical stimulation and gratification such as kissing, embracing, caressing, and direct genital contact. In this report, the word will be used with a wider reference than genital union; sex is considered here as an elemental force or drive that promotes life and that

has a variety of physiological and psychological manifestations at every age level. As such, it can be a force for pleasure, tenderness, and human relatedness. The report emphasizes these positive aspects of sex in human life. While we recognize that sex can be and not infrequently is used destructively, the focus of the study is not on pathology but on sexuality as a normal and varied phenomenon of man's entire life span.

2. Sexuality is an important force in every personality that influences the individual's relationships with others and his adaptation to his environment and that, in turn, is influenced by all the other unique attributes of the personality. Throughout the life cycle, sex is an evolving, dynamic force that can be understood only in relation to the rest of development at any particular phase. Behavior patterns in late adolescence are not necessarily permanent—they may express a temporary adaptation.

3. In no institution did we find published or printed materials that explicitly stated its views toward sexual conduct on the campus, yet institutions widely assume that student behavior will reflect the college rules and regulations. If the college is concerned with the individual growth of the student, official pronouncements need to take adolescent sexuality explicitly into account. If a college has certain expectations about sexual conduct on the campus, it has a responsibility to clarify them. There is also need to provide information about the responsibility to self and to others that is implicit in undertaking sexual relations.

4. Basic to the approach of this study and to the "Guidelines" in particular is the assumption that the college assigns primary value to the individual and that it is prepared to stand as buffer between the student and outside (or internal) pressures of opinion, including unfavorable publicity. In a disciplinary case concerning sex such a stance may be required to insure that the individual's life situation, assets, and limitations will be considered and respected. We also assume that the educational pur-

pose of the college requires exploration of what is psychologically and educationally sound. For example, a case of out-of-wedlock pregnancy calls for careful and realistic counseling.

5. It is impossible to generalize about the psychological meaning of an isolated sexual episode in an individual's life because a variety of factors—developmental, biological, social, and individual—may influence a single incident of sexual behavior especially in adolescence. Range and level of understanding can vary greatly, depending on knowledge of the person involved and the setting in which a single instance occurs. For this reason, we urge that disciplinary cases involving sexual behavior on the campus be examined in their broad context of the specific personal and environmental influences involved.

6. Within the framework of these assumptions, we believe there is great potential for flexibility. Widely varying philosophies prevail on American campuses. It would be impossible, even if it were desirable, to suggest a single set of parietal rules that would suit all colleges. We hope the report will be of value to college officers and others not because it suggests specific solutions, but because it sets some important aspects of late adolescent sexuality in perspective as part of human development and points out some ways in which both the developmental needs of the individual and the educational purposes of the college may be served.

1

THE DEVELOPMENT AND INTEGRATION OF SEXUALITY IN THE PERSONALITY

Sexual Development in Childhood

". . . The sexual instincts of man do not suddenly awaken between the thirteenth and fifteenth year, i.e. at puberty, but operate from the outset of the child's development, change gradually from one form to another, progress from one state to another, until at last adult sexual life is achieved as the final result from this long series of developments."[*] Thus Anna Freud, before a group of teachers 30 years ago, described the concept of sexuality that today dominates our understanding of sexual development.

Psychological investigations of adults and children have shown the important contribution of early life experience to the development of mature sexuality; however, the physical changes of adolescence herald the emerging adult so noticeably that the significant relationship of the earlier life of the child to this adult sexual behavior tends to be obscured. Pleasure-seeking behavior begins in infancy and is continually modified as the child develops. The adult pattern of sexual behavior represents a composite of many different maturational elements to which each phase of childhood experience has contributed its important part.

---

[*] Freud, Anna: Psychoanalysis for Teachers and Parents, Beacon Press, Inc., Boston, 1935; paperback by arrangement with Emerson Books, Inc., 1960, pp. 71-72.

Implications of Childhood Development for Adult Behavior

Early physical contact with the mother gives the infant an awareness of his own body and, ultimately, of the separateness of the mother as another person who provides gratification of physical needs and satisfying human contact. These early experiences are important in the later formation of a sense of separate identity, and in the achievement of the ability to turn to others for meaningful human interaction in satisfying the needs of the self. Early experience with dependable, repeated satisfactions lays the groundwork for the capacity to trust that later on makes adult enduring relationships possible.

Parental attitudes toward the child's bodily functions influence the child's attitude toward his own body and his ability to feel pleasure in his bodily activities. Learning to accept limits on behavior set by parents is an important step toward the child's ultimate adult capacity to control his emotions and his sexual behavior. The discipline thus established eventually channels feelings into appropriate social forms of expression and develops the ability to delay immediate satisfactions for longer-range goals.

The child has his first opportunity to express his own capacity for loving with his parents. He is enabled to value this capacity by loving his parents and feeling that his love is valued by them. Childhood loving is possessive, and inevitably brings the child into conflict with others. The resulting conflict and competition can generate future difficulties, but, more often, they stimulate him to develop mature forms of loving that do not depend on exclusive possession. The child is also aware of the quality of his parents' relation to each other, and this relationship serves as his first model. Later on, he may seek to emulate or avoid their patterns of behavior.

Persisting Patterns of Childhood Pleasure-Seeking Behavior

No child progresses through his development completely

smoothly and without difficulty. Each child tends to cling to the particular behavior patterns that gratify and help him to deal with stress. For example, when a child reacts to frustration by wanting to be taken care of and comforted, he may express his wish through the physical act of leaning against and seeking to be held by a parent. The extent to which such pleasure seeking activities of childhood persist depends on their importance in the individual's development.

At certain stages of growth, one or another of the various components of childhood sexuality may assume disproportionate emphasis until it can be integrated with the rest of the personality. Childhood masturbation, for example, may assume importance as one aspect of experimentation with physical pleasure as an end in itself; or the activity may represent the child's affirmation of his sexuality as his own, through exerting his own capacity to take charge of it. When he no longer needs to prove this component as his own, the behavior becomes less necessary.

Prior to adolescent biological maturation, very important experiences with pleasure-seeking behavior have taken place that become components of the adolescent and the later adult sexual pattern. As he moves into adulthood, the adolescent's relationships begin to take the needs of others more fully into account; they also reflect his own individuality and assume more of a quality of give and take. These changes have parallels in his sexual life, where ultimate pleasure is increasingly sought through sexual intercourse, while the bodily pleasures of early childhood find expression in sexual foreplay.

Sexual Development in Adolescence

Each period of development presents specific challenges. How an individual deals with these demands is influenced by his biological endowment, his previous life experience, and the alternatives that his own culture makes possible at each stage of growth. It is difficult, therefore, to speak of universal characteristics of the late adolescent period. Culture so influences the complexity of adolescence that societies undergoing rapid change pose a wide range of problems for the late adolescent.

Influence of the Culture

The initiation rites of primitive societies announce to the adolescent, his family, and the broader community that he has reached man's estate. In the ambiguity of American life, there is no consensus about the age, attainments, or other conditions that determine adulthood, nor is the role of the emerging adult clearly defined. The range of adult roles and responsibilities in a sophisticated society are broad and complex, and present potential conflict for the adolescent. Adolescents themselves often search out critical life experiences that they feel will confirm their adult status.

American society has been characterized as providing a socially sanctioned moratorium between childhood and adulthood. The dependency expected of children is tolerated and reinforced by the unavailability of full adult status long after the young person becomes physically mature. The adolescent periodically displays childlike behavior that ranges from the dependent to the provocative and defiant. At the same time he is developing confidence, independence, and socially responsible behavior. The focus of his significant relationships shifts from family and home to the peer group and to certain adults, who are accepted as models distinct from parents. New relationships and identifications formed in adolescence further the process of the individual's maturation within the society at large.

Response of the Personality to the Upsurge of Drive

Rapid changes of a physical, psychological, and social nature occur as the individual moves from childhood to adulthood. Whatever the culture, one of the challenges in this period involves the adolescent's coming to grips with changes in himself, both biological and psychological, that accompany accentuated sexual drives. The young person emerges from late childhood with attitudes that he learned as a child, that were appropriate for a child, and that accepted parental aims. The equilibrium established during latency (when the drives are reduced in intensity) is easily upset by the upsurge of biological drive announcing puberty.

The adolescent reacts with varying unconscious patterns of defense derived from this period and earlier childhood. Not only must he contend with the new and urgent genital component of the drive, but earlier childhood components of sexuality are reawakened as well. These early manifestations of sexuality are associated with primitive behavior and fantasy and with ambivalence. These feelings may be painful for the young person and bring him into conflict with those around him. Since one or the other parent has until now been the object of these drives, the parents' very existence is threatening to the adolescent, who may find it necessary to reject them as models and as objects of his sexual and affectionate strivings.

Some young people deny themselves almost any form of pleasure and adopt ascetic attitudes in reaction to the accentuated sexual drive. Some use their enhanced ability to think abstractly to protect themselves from dangerous and forbidden feelings. They attempt to deal with emotions as though they were ideas. Some can accept sexual strivings with a degree of comfort and can integrate them more easily with other facets of the personality so that they become part of the changing self-concept.

Changing Self-Awareness

At this time, when his picture of himself is changing, the adolescent becomes aware of new expectations by the people who are important to him. Thus, one of the most important tasks of the late adolescent is to integrate disparate aspects of his personality into a stabilized, unique, separate identity that can be confirmed and supported by his social milieu. Adolescence proceeds relatively smoothly for some; for others, it is turbulent and is characterized by temporary periods of marked anxiety and disorganization, followed by the evolution of better-integrated patterns. Still other adolescents experience severe disorganization of their personalities that inhibits or arrests further development. Such periods of extreme disturbance may be triggered by experiences that require commitment on the part of the adolescent for which he is not ready. These may range from sexual relationships to stringent academic demands or competition.

Adolescents frequently feel uncertain about their sexual identity. They become frightened of aspects of themselves that they fear contradict their own image of masculinity or femininity. They may undergo periods of confusion when earlier conflicts about sexual identity are revived. In childhood, the individual has identified himself with characteristics of both parents; it is never a question of a girl's identifying herself solely with her mother or a boy's identifying himself only with his father. The boy's personality is enriched by qualities of his mother, as the girl's is enriched by qualities of her father. Awareness of characteristics associated with the parent of the opposite sex can at first be confusing to the late adolescent, but comfortable integration of the various elements of his identity requires acceptance of both.

Some Reactions to the Opportunity for Sexual Relationships

At this time, too, the American adolescent encounters courtship behavior as it is defined in his particular community. He learns the current rituals for initiating contact with members of the opposite sex and discovers that dating patterns assume great significance. From the broader culture, his unique family upbringing, and the values of his own peer group, he evolves a code of sexual conduct that can provide him with his own guidelines for behavior. While he experiments in increased intimacy with a member of the opposite sex, the adolescent ultimately seeks fulfillment of himself as a sexual person and confirmation of his total identity.

Sexual experience may seem threatening for a number of reasons. It may engender feelings of guilt that stem from prohibitions of early childhood, it may represent the loss of the protected status of the child, or it may produce fears of being overwhelmed by feelings of too great intensity. Such anxieties are dealt with in a variety of ways by adolescents experiencing them. For example, such phenomena as panty raids among college students illustrate the temporary ascendancy of a childish, and presumably safer, form of sexual behavior. Group sexual activities involving, for example, several young men and one girl may be another expression of unwillingness to commit one's self to an intense emotional relationship between two people. Deviant sexual patterns become more understandable when viewed as persisting childhood forms of sexual gratification that may represent an effort of the young person to protect himself from the anxieties and conflicts of sexual maturation. Anxiety about homosexuality or about one's sexual adequacy may engender frantic repeated heterosexual attempts; or the defense may be turning to one's own body as the only safe object for sexual activity; or efforts may be directed at denial of sexuality altogether.

Pressures of the Transition to Heterosexual Commitment

Late adolescence provides new pressures and new opportunities for release of emotional tensions through sexual activities. Some adolescents exhibit little tolerance of frustration, and while they may talk about the virtues of freedom, they are in fact often at the mercy of their impulses. Freedom in this context, as everywhere in the human condition, requires the capacity to tolerate frustration, to consider consequences of action, to act on conviction and in consonance with one's own goals; in short, to choose.

Some adolescents become preoccupied with the physical aspects of sexuality. This tendency may be accentuated by a literature and culture that abound in the treatment of sex as a detached physical skill. Most late adolescents, however, are as eager to arrive at moral and emotional standards for their sexual behavior as they are to learn about the anatomical and physiological aspects of sex.

Many adolescents are not ready for long-term heterosexual relationships with all the emotional commitment and responsibility involved, and many will wish to divorce the physical aspects of sexual experience from personal commitment. This separation often represents a way of protecting themselves from their own immaturity and incapacity for commitment. In the past, this phenomenon was more characteristic of young men than of young women. Young women more often sought to restrict sexual activity to those relationships that had meaning for them. Presumably, this difference was due both to biological distinctions and to the fact of pregnancy as the inherent difference between the consequences of sexual union for the man and the woman. Current experience on the campus, however, indicates that sexual activity has become almost as common among girls as boys and postponement of sexual activity until marriage is less pronounced. This apparent shift in feminine attitudes is one of the clearly revolutionary elements in the current sexual "revolution."

Failure to Achieve Heterosexuality

Eventually, adolescents grow up. The majority achieve the capacity for pleasurable sexual activity associated with a sustained, meaningful relationship. Some, who are unable to relinquish one or another aspect of immaturity, persist in compartmentalized sexual activity without experiencing commitment or even affectionate feelings toward their partners. Everyone knows that adolescents (among others) often confuse sex with love. It may be more accurate to say that some of them are able to permit themselves sexuality only through the unconscious stratagem of calling it love. This maneuver may be successful in temporarily bypassing a puritanical conscience, but a delayed and exorbitant price is exacted when relationships based entirely on erotic feelings later prove to be insupportable on any basis.

Individuals who suffer severe disturbance in their psychological development may be unable to establish socially acceptable patterns of sexual behavior. Fixed patterns of homosexual behavior, for example, usually indicate deep anxieties stemming from earlier periods of development. The determinants are many, but they may be illustrated by one example: a boy deprived of a usual father-son relationship may later be unable to relinquish a continuing symbolic search for a father through homosexual activity in favor of heterosexual relationships more appropriate to his chronological development. Similarly, a girl may seek a sustaining relationship with a maternal figure through homosexual behavior. Sexual behavior not generally condoned by society, and stemming from incompletely resolved phases of early development, may represent the only close human contact possible for such individuals. For others, it represents only a passing stage of development.

The Search for Identity

Still another task faces adolescents as they approach adulthood: they must increase their independence from their families and at the same time form a new relationship with their parents. In many segments of American society, a high premium is placed on the early achievement of independence. College students, for example, are not expected to rely heavily and continuously on their parents although it is anticipated that family ties will be maintained. For many young people, this increased autonomy is simply an extension of a series of experiences that have prepared them for independent living. Others find it difficult to separate from dependent or affectionate childhood ties; they may exhibit an exaggerated sense of independence to convince themselves and others that they can stand on their own feet. The need to relinquish these strong attachments and to establish new kinds of relationships with persons outside of the family is one of the developmental challenges of this period.

Self-regulation and the Emerging Self-image

As an emerging adult, the late adolescent may focus too literally on a single criterion as a definition of maturity and adulthood. For example, he may emphasize the power to earn money as the essential ingredient of an adult identity, but he may fail to recognize that the same issues of productivity are involved in his college work. Faced with a necessary delay in assuming a remunerative work role, the college student may turn to sex as a vehicle for asserting that he has or should have adult status.

The college student deals with his academic work in a context that differs markedly from his experience in high school. He must come to grips with the responsibility of regulating himself in his work; there are fewer external sources of control for him to rely upon; and he must cope with the freedom to use his time creatively. While the increased freedom seems welcome to most students, it becomes seductive and burdensome for those who lack self-discipline. These students find difficulty in assuming an active learning role; they expect and seek out the same dependent relationship with their teachers that they sought in high school. Other students rebel against the rules or the freedom offered by the college as a part of the process of separating themselves from parental authority, sometimes at considerable cost to the central educational purpose.

The student also discovers whether or not his view of himself in relation to his high school peers is confirmed at college. Hopefully, the larger psychological and social world of the campus provides new challenges to his capabilities and thus enables him to gain a more realistic view of himself. At the same time, he continues to develop his own system of values. At college, the student is faced with a broadened exposure to a range of ideas and values that he may not have confronted before. Some of the new political, religious, and social ideas may collide with his parents' or his own past views and may stimulate constructive conflict leading to reappraisal and growth.

The Influence of Peers and of Friendships with Adults

Because of the urgency of establishing independence during this developmental period, it is not surprising that the college student turns to his peer group for support as he asserts his independence from his family. The campus usually provides a variety of peer groups with which the adolescent may ally himself. The degree of identity that the student has already achieved will influence his choice of groups and the choice will, in turn, influence his further development. His friends will provide important support in this transition period. For example, within the small social group, the student may feel more free to explore new ideas and new attitudes, and to experiment with possible new roles for himself. Friendships provide a valuable source of security and acceptance during the adolescent's moves toward more autonomy in relation to his family. At the same time, friendships place the adolescent under strong pressures to conform to the values of his peer group. These pressures may be quite compelling in determining the pattern of his sexual behavior.

Students also seek allies in the adult world. Trusted adults may substitute for the trusted parents of childhood as the adolescent extends his emotional range beyond the family; adult friends may serve as models for young people in the process of relinquishing immature patterns of behavior and they can also serve as a bulwark against the peer pressure. Sometimes, a strong attachment is formed to an older person who represents an idealized parent or a combination of mother and father. These relationships, where they represent only repetition of parental relationships, lead to inertia in development. However, to the extent that they provide new experience in close, secure relationships, they have the potential of extending growth beyond the pattern afforded by family and thereby serve as another pathway toward adult identity.

Identity and Sexuality

The capacity for a mature sexual relationship is intimately linked with a sense of personal identity; the boy is ready to assume the role of the man. In addition to personal feelings of adequacy and gratification comes an acceptance of the responsibilities and satisfactions of adult relationships, including those of having and raising children.

Individuals vary in their progress toward establishing a sense of identity. An adolescent whose need for closeness has been frustrated or overindulged in childhood frequently grasps at sex now that it becomes available, and premature commitments follow. Sex may also serve primarily to demonstrate dominance or to express hostility toward the opposite sex. Also at work among adolescents are cultural and psychological pressures to validate one's masculinity or femininity through sexual experiences. In the American culture, with its uneasy tolerance of closeness among men, the male student may seek out a girl to confide in and the relationship may become a sexual one.

In these instances sexual intimacy has its base in needs related to the uncertainties of the emerging identity; the relationship is mechanical and self-centered in contrast to the mutuality and commitment associated with mature sexual involvement.

The Relationship Between Sexual and Intellectual Development

To many people, there is little apparent relationship between the intellectual and the sexual drives. A traditional separation of mind and body and a distinction between man's lower (physical) and higher (mental) functions have supported this attitude. Yet, bodily needs and intellectual processes are closely linked from infancy.

In Early Childhood

The demands of the infant and the young child for immediate satisfaction of his needs bring about the development of imagination during the frustrating wait for satisfaction. Children construct a fantasy world that insures satisfaction and security in ways that the real world never can. They also come to delight in their imaginative thinking for its own sake and to enjoy the fantasies of others in stories, fairy tales, and pictures. Later on the pleasures of the arts and of literature stimulate and enrich their imaginations.

The small child's early researches into the world around him begin with simple perception. By responding to the child's curiosity parents support the accuracy of his perceptions and encourage his acquisition of the capacity for a secure grasp on reality. In addition, the pleasure experienced by the child will stimulate his incentive for perceptual and intellectual exploration and for mastery of the outside world. The child's investigations are not handicapped by any lack of clarity in his own perceptions or reasoning power, but he may be severely hampered when adults fail to provide straightforward confirmation of some of the accurate observations and reasoning he has achieved. For example, parents may deny elements in their own relationship about which they are uncomfortable (commonly the sexual relationship or the fact of friction between them) when the child perceives these. This denial has special significance for the child of 4 to 6, for at this time there occurs a combination of intellectual curiosity and intense attachment to the parents that leaves the child particularly vulnerable to conflict between his perceptions and contradiction of them by trusted adults. If his perceptions are made light of, or if he is reprimanded because of them, the child may be uneasy about using his intellect and giving free rein to his curiosity. When parental denial is sufficiently severe in significant areas, the child may become reluctant or unwilling to use his intellect; or he may himself accept and employ this imposed rejection of what he perceives. In both instances, his educability is impaired.

In Latency

Between the ages of 6 and 11, there is a period of respite for the child when his sexual drives decrease in intensity. Up until this period the child's behavior is principally guided by external factors, the hope of love or the threat of punishment. In latency he continues the development of a conscience modeled upon parental prohibitions as he has perceived them, and continues evolving an ideal for himself based upon his view of parental attributes and expectations. Equipped with these rudimentary internal controls the child moves beyond the family for the first time into school. Normally, this interim allows the child to develop his capacities for work, for learning, and for practical mastery of the world around him, with relative freedom from sexual preoccupations.

In Puberty

With the resurgence of biological drives during adolescence, the young person's immediate reaction to his sexual and aggressive feelings will, in large part, derive from attitudes toward the drives learned earlier in childhood. His response will be influenced also by his current life situation with his parents, the values of his peer group, and his level of intellectual development. Personality development in adolescence includes maturation of the capacity for more complex ways of thinking. These thoughts expand the possibilities of experience and are given voice through the endless discussions familiar to all observers of adolescents. This talk partly serves as an intellectualized exploration of alternative commitments in a kind of dress rehearsal for later adult perspectives on such issues as personal values and vocational and marriage choices.

Defensive Uses of the Intellect

The adolescent can also use his new intellectual potential in defensive ways to protect himself from disturbing inner conflicts about his own sexual feelings. Thus, he may deal with feelings as though they were simply ideas to be thought about. For example, instead of expressing affection directly, some adolescents may talk endlessly about "the true meaning" of a relationship. The talking represents the drive by ideas and thus prevents the feeling from finding outlet into immediate action. Or, ideas may provide the adolescent with a rationalization for certain types of non-rational sexual activity that are difficult to face directly. For example, a student bent on seduction may justify his action on grounds of physical and psychological health, while in fact he is propelled by unconscious needs other than biological ones. He may, for example, have no conscious awareness that he has based his self-esteem on demonstrating his sexual prowess to his peer group. Unable to free himself from this pressure or to face it, he protects himself by erecting a barricade of highly intellectualized reasoning.

The defensive use of intellect may lead in several different directions. When the intellect has been used mainly as a weapon for the suppression of underlying emotional conflicts, the intense investment in the intellect may wither away once the disturbing drives have been integrated into the personality. This is what happens to the boy genius who seems "burned out" intellectually at the age of 25. Or, intellectualizing can become a permanent defense. We all know the person who thinks only in ideological or doctrinaire terms, or the compulsive talker who becomes more attached to words than to the world of people. For most people, however, the intellect is eventually freed for full development as sexual drives are accepted and as internal controls for their expression are established. Intellect then becomes available in greater measure for the pursuit of a knowledgeable mastery of one's environment.

The continued growth of the intellect is enhanced by a comfortable acceptance of instinctual drives; the intellect and instinctual energy, when they exist in friendly relationship in the personality, can act together to further the over-all psychological purposes of the individual. Instinctual energy is an ally, not an enemy, in the process of education.

The Challenge of Simultaneous Emotional and Intellectual Development

It has been suggested that from a developmental point of view the four years of college come at the worst possible time in the schedule of biological and emotional development.* For many individuals, the internal thrust toward emotional and sexual maturity collides in an abundance of apparently undirected energy with the demands of intellectual discipline or the social requirements of an orderly college community. Society expects of the college student that he simultaneously complete emotional, sexual, and intellectual development and that he meet radically increased standards of achievement.

Not all students can so schedule their biological progression to fit this external demand. Unduly rigid institutional requirements may seriously interfere with intellectual development, even among the intellectually gifted, by propelling the student toward premature closure of developmental possibilities. Under these circumstances the cost in intellectual potential is high, both to

---

* We are indebted to Miss Anna Freud in conversations with the Committee for this idea about the dual demands simultaneously confronting college students.

society and to those students who do not mature within the usual pattern. The widely publicized problem of dropouts and recent evidence of greater flexibility in college policies toward transfer and leave of absence may testify that we have been expecting the impossible of many of our young people. Greater understanding of the requirements of individual growth and rate of development, together with flexible administrative handling, gives promise of a broader opportunity for intellectual fulfillment.

The Relationship Between Adolescence and the Adult World

It is healthy that adolescence disrupts childhood adaptations and changes the child's relationships with adults and with his peers. With disruption comes not only emotional turmoil, but also a second chance for the individual to repeat, modify, and complete developmental processes that were begun earlier within the family. The turmoil, including return of childish modes of behavior in the adolescent, therefore implies a potentiality for growth when new learning can take place.

Parents

It cannot be denied that this potential of adolescent behavior is often obscured and frequently puts the stability and maturity of his parents and other adults to a severe test. Though there will necessarily be times when whatever the adult does is wrong, to the extent that adults understand their own importance (and lack of it) to the late adolescent, the rewards will be greater and the upsets less in their contacts with college students. Maturational changes take time, and until these processes are well along, preoccupation with "impulse control" may be temporarily predominant over other requirements. Eventually, with personality reorganization, the upsurging biological drives no longer disrupt, but become a major source of energy for adult activities.

Geographical and social mobility, rapid technological change, urbanization and increase in population have altered established patterns of behavior, with a resulting challenge to traditional attitudes. Although educated parents are increasingly aware of their own importance to the mental health of their young children, they appear to be losing confidence in their own abilities to raise them. They turn to experts for advice, and their children's schools, willingly or unwillingly, assume the role of experts in childrearing. The clear corollary of this phenomenon is that parents assign ever greater responsibility to the school for the personality development of their children. Another aspect of this parental abdication is an increasing degree of isolation of children in their own peer groups and in the sub-culture of the school, where they have little need or opportunity to function in the larger social order into which they must eventually move.

Adults Outside the Family

At other historical periods, children have had assigned roles and tasks that were appropriate to their age and capabilities and that made real contributions to family life and the adult community. From these activities, children learned what was possible for them and what was expected of them, both as children and in direct anticipation of adulthood. The substantial reduction in meaningful work by children through technology is complicated by commercial emphasis on a child-centered world. Both serve to isolate children and limit their collaboration with adults.

This separation from real adult concerns that the adolescent experiences in childhood compounds his difficulties as he attempts to assume adult patterns and values. He finds, too, that the adult world is not prepared to welcome him fully into its system of work, pleasure, responsibilities, and rewards. He is still several years away from full occupational and social status, particularly if he is embarked upon an extended program of higher education. Often, he encounters adult jealousy, fear, anger, or rejection of his exuberant or bizarre expressions of adolescent impulses. His dilemma is further complicated by the fact that he himself needs to keep adults at arm's length so that he can establish himself as an autonomous person. He may attempt to gain the semblance of adult status through marriage. He may rebel against the adult world by "hitting back" with unacceptable or delinquent behavior. He may create or participate in a special, rebellious youth culture, for example, that of the British Mods or of our own bohemians and beatniks. Other young people, many of them, tolerate their intermediate status and accept the fact that the achievement of adult status will require further study or work or both.

Values and Controls

In the matter of managing sexual drive, the late adolescent's problems are compounded by the fact that the adult world itself has no clear standards of behavior. This may become apparent to the young person as close at hand as his own home; he certainly cannot miss the message in contemporary fiction, movies, and plays. In the movies and popular press, the treatment of sex is often feverish and lurid. At the opposite extreme, current research with its statistical computation of various physical acts emphasizes the physical aspects of sex to the neglect of the broader personal elements of the relationship. Many of the marriage manuals also emphasize a physical and clinical focus. Small wonder that the young adult is not sure what his society expects of him sexually.

There have always been both internal and external sanctions that operate to control sexual behavior. Effective internal controls have always included conscience, self-expectations, or the desire for making sex part of a meaningful relationship. External factors, such as disapproval by persons important to one's self, the customs of one's social group, or retaliatory loss of privilege, esteem, or financial support, have been and still can be potent means of control. Some other external sanctions seem, however, to have lost much of their former power. For example, the double standard is changing. Venereal disease and fear of pregnancy have been substantially reduced, owing to medical advances (although the incidence of venereal disease is currently increasing). Threats of social ostracism and religious rejection do not mean as much as they once did. As the power of former controls wanes, the emotional climate of the relationship as a determinant of the degree of sexual involvement has become more important. Though they have rejected the moral prohibitions of an earlier generation, some students today have substituted an idealism and strict morality of their own. We see them suffering disappointment when they fail to achieve an idealized relationship, characteristically an almost perfect one of mutual harmony and unselfish consideration. When the weakening of traditional controls is added to the problem of communication between generations, it becomes clear that the late adolescent must face not only the predictable inner uncertainties and confusions of this phase of his growth but also an external world that is distinguished neither by clarity of demands nor firmness of direction nor understanding of his problems.

2

SEXUAL ISSUES ON THE CAMPUS

Heterosexual Behavior

There is general agreement that premarital sexual relations among undergraduate college students are more frequent than they were a generation ago. Certainly, students are more open about their activities and more vocal about their prerogatives. This change reflects tolerance of behavior that would have been almost universally censured a few decades ago and that is still severely questioned in many places. Twenty-five years ago, a college boy seeking sexual experience most often chose a girl of a different social class whom he would not consider marrying; today, the partner of the boy is likely to be a girl of similar class and background; in addition, college girls themselves often initiate sexual activity. With the revised concept of the female role, girls are becoming more concerned with the development of their sexual freedom and expression. The following case illustrates some of these issues.

Case Example

Sally was an especially gifted student, interested in her work, and gave promise of a successful creative career. In high school, she had had her eye on getting into a good college. She had not been active in the social life of school, which seemed to her superficial. In her freshman year at college, she threw herself into a whirl of active dating, received many invitations, and was very popular. When she had satisfied herself that she was desirable and could carry off social occasions well, some of the excitement of dating began to pall and she sought more meaningful relationships. She now dated only boys with whom she felt she could establish a deeper emotional and intellectual relationship. One of the boys she came to know better wanted to have sexual relations. She described her reaction: "For me it is a special thing. I am sort of monogamous. I don't like to diffuse to a lot of people. I like to have close friends even though I know a lot of people. As far as I am concerned, intercourse is one thing where you are giving a lot of yourself to one person. I never wanted to do it unless I was absolutely sure about that person and I never was; particularly when I started realizing that these people did not care much about my welfare or about me as a person. It impressed me as if they almost had to prove to themselves and also to other people that they could do it. It was a competitive thing."

Sally had not expected to engage in sexual relations in college. In her junior year, however, she met a boy who, she said, was "interested in my interests and I was interested in his interests." Eventually, they had intercourse. Here is her description of her feelings: "It got to the point where it really got frustrating not doing it. We had been going out together seven or eight months and it seemed—if you feel strongly about a person and if you really love him—I don't see anything really wrong about it, because it is a complete relationship, as complete as for some people who get married. This is one action where you give everything you have to the other person. There is always a circumstance of holding back and it would have been wrong; it would have been almost wrong to keep holding back something that I really wanted to give him.

Discussion

Sally reflects the concerns of many young people. In her attempt to make decisions, she recognized clearly the special nature of her relationship with this particular boy and made the judgment that it warranted intimacy. She rejected what she perceived to be the competitive motivation in sex. Some aggressiveness normally plays a part in sexual relations, but to the extent that desire for conquest dominates a relationship, it undermines the rewards of mutuality for the participants. At college, it was important to Sally at first to succeed in dating competition. If she had not been successful, one might speculate whether or not subsequent sexual intimacy might have represented something else—a proof of desirability, for example, or a substitute for the gratification of feeling accepted and appreciated by her peers.

Growth is shown by Sally's ability to develop flexible attitudes toward the possibility of intercourse. Her values appear to be consistent. She demonstrates a responsiveness to life experience and a capacity to learn from them and to make choices. Rigidity, the necessity to cling unyieldingly to a fixed set of attitudes without the exercise of judgment, is usually indicative of anxiety and a lack of freedom to learn.

Motivation and Sexual Behavior

We misread the message conveyed by college students in their discussions and demands in the sexual area if we see only defense of the pursuit of pleasure. Under the guise of asking for sexual freedom, the student may be concerned with such fundamentals as identity, relatedness, and security. Those students whose sexual activity goes more or less unnoticed probably represent a large middle group who handle their sexual life privately and without its being an apparent problem to themselves or to others. Their activities may include intercourse or they may be limited to petting (which in an adult context would constitute foreplay as a prelude to intercourse), but in any event do not come to the notice of authorities. It is well worth noting that promiscuity characterizes only a few individuals on each college campus, although these cases, frequently inflated by publicity, are often conspicuous. For the majority of students, increased experience with their heterosexuality is a lonely and painful search in a vital area of life which many adults are unable to discuss comfortably.

Sexual relationships serve many functions. For the girl, even a brief sexual intimacy may provide a temporary sense of being wanted; she may assume that nothing else she has to offer would be of equal interest to her partner. Although this view might have a neurotic basis indicating low self-esteem, it could also be a healthy awareness that nothing else would reassure or satisfy the young man with whom she is importantly involved. A more neurotic pattern is apparent where the individual uses sexual intimacy to handle feelings of depression, emptiness, and dependency. In such circumstances, the importance of the relationship lies only in seeking a sense of closeness as a temporary haven against loneliness and other anxieties. Compulsive sexual activity usually represents an unresolved conflict and an attempt to relieve anxiety rather than simple pursuit of pleasure. Behavior that has an exaggerated quality of urgency often serves a defensive purpose not recognized by the individual.

Young men and women attempt to express and confirm identity through physical intimacy, and sexuality is employed toward this end in various ways. The range extends from demonstration of prowess, aggression, and dominance to more complex modes of interaction in which the mutuality of the relationship between two people is the major aspect of self-fulfillment. Although pride in conquest is commonly attributed to boys, it also excites many girls. When sex is used solely to prove power and dominance, sexual expression can veer in pathological directions.

The need of men to confirm their sexual capacity has long been recognized. Sexual proficiency and the achievement of satisfaction by women has also been recognized as important, but it is currently a matter of intense concern among young women. Sometimes both partners behave as though the adequacy and self-esteem of each was dependent on whether or not the woman achieves orgasm or even on whether their orgasms occur simultaneously. This sort of exaggerated emphasis not only can create undesirable tension in the sexual act itself, but can devalue important satisfactions in other areas of the relationship as well.

The peer group pressure to engage in and to be considered competent in sexual intercourse drives both girls and boys further, at times, than they feel ready to go. They may look to external rules, regulations, and limitations as a way of providing relief from their own ambivalence and anxiety about sexual experience. The use of rules as protection represents an entirely different concept from the more commonly accepted idea that rules control behavior. Rules may provide a shelter for the student who is unable to resolve internal conflicts or who is unready to assume responsibility for determining his own standards of behavior.

Issues of sexual morality are complex and confusing for the college student. The oversimplification of the moral position in which abstinence equals right and indulgence equals wrong is not at all consistent with actual conduct at most colleges or in society at large. This paradox raises conflicts for many young people when they experiment and require of themselves a reworking of their childhood in relation to new experience. In an atmosphere where students freely engage in sexual relations, the student who does so is part of an accepted and larger pattern even though the activity itself is disapproved of by some members of the community. His acts have a different significance from those of the student who enters into the same acts in an environment where sexual relationships rarely occur. The necessity for secrecy, for instance, underscores the implication of wrong-doing and may mobilize elements of guilt. In search of criteria by which to consider sexual relations prior to marriage, students often conclude that sex with love is right and moral, sex without love is not. While sexual intercourse between people who find it pleasurable, assume responsibility for their acts, and

have respect for each other's feelings is different from sex used
for sadistic or exploitive purposes, the role of passion and idealism in love relationships may blur these distinctions. Abstinence,
at the other extreme, may simply reflect inability to embrace
sexual pleasure during adolescence.

Summary

Throughout his adolescent sexual experience, the individual
is preparing himself for his mature adult sexual role. His relationships in adolescence may be primarily pleasure-seeking or
thrill-seeking, or they may serve developmental needs for closeness, or for group acceptance. This is a time when, for some
adolescents, experimentation may be important, commitment
would be premature, and something is to be gained from a
transitory relationship. But for other students such liaisons
would produce conflict and anxiety because they believe that
sex, marriage, and responsible parenthood are inseparable; their
satisfactory sexual development will require a relationship that
either meets or anticipates meeting these criteria. Progress toward sexual maturity is measured in part by the degree of respect of the participants for each other as well as by the absence
of manipulation, exploitation, and compulsion in the relationship. Successful maturity also eventually requires the capacity
to combine sexual pleasure with a member of the opposite sex
with other life goals, responsibilities, and experiences. Some
individuals achieve this much earlier or later than others.

Contraception, Pregnancy, and Abortion

Although attitudes towards premarital sexual relations vary,
it can be stated unequivocally that premarital pregnancy during the college years is usually a seriously if not disastrously dis-
ruptive event. Out-of-wedlock pregnancy has of course vastly
different implications for the young woman than for the young
man, but for both it represents an important life crisis. For the

girl, almost all the available alternatives (precipitous marriage, abortion, giving the baby up for adoption) represent solutions that inevitably cause serious emotional stress, and her college career may be interrupted or ended. For the boy too, it will have serious repercussions, whether he finds himself in the position of prematurely assuming emotional and financial responsibility for a family or whether he attempts to withdraw from the situation, to be faced later with repercussions of conflict and guilt. Unexpected pregnancy even in a married student may cause considerable strain, although the emotional turmoil obviously is of a different magnitude. Thus, the prevention of pregnancy during the college years through abstinence or the use of contraceptives is an important matter for students as well as for many other individuals less directly involved (administrators, faculty, and parents). In connection with these issues, a host of urgent questions arise that have far-reaching implications for the educational and emotional development of the students themselves and that profoundly affect other lives as well.

Contraception

Although contraceptives have long been available, there has unquestionably been an increase recently in the accessibility of contraceptive information and materials despite certain religious and legal obstacles to their use. Many college students view contraceptive information as a right that is due them. They are informed about methods and interested in the new oral contraceptives as offering safe and relatively easy protection; a large number of knowledgeable students seem to make effective use of contraceptives as the occasion requires.

Despite increasing sophistication, complexities and problems in the use of contraceptives persist. One arresting paradox is the number of unintended pregnancies that occur despite the availability of contraceptives. Some young adults are simply ignorant of the relevant facts. Others, familiar with the information, fail to act in accordance with it for reasons based in unconscious motivation and conflict.

Young people who need to deny their sexual concerns frequently seek refuge in romanticizing, and they may, for example, feel that mechanical devices interfere with the "sincerity, spontaneity, and beauty" of the sexual act. Adolescents, filled with idealism and romantic feeling, passionate, eager to experiment but frightened at the same time, may not find it easy to acknowledge uncertainty as beginners when the need to use practical contraceptive techniques arises at the very moment they feel that their manhood or womanhood is challenged. Significant, too, is the fact that use of contraceptives does in fact require conscious recognition of the intention to engage in sexual intercourse. Experimenting adolescents frequently seek to avoid this full awareness. For example, a girl may feel that the planning involved in the use of a diaphragm or pills implies a stronger commitment to frequent sexual intercourse or to a particular relationship with its attendant problems than she is prepared to undertake.

The emphasis on individual differences among students throughout this report applies here as well. Those students who habitually deal with life by avoiding the recognition of unpleasant reality will frequently neglect to use contraceptives. The young man may fail to procure or carry condoms because he is embarrassed and can easily avoid confronting his feelings by rationalizing that there will be no need for them. The committee feels that this tendency may be reinforced in colleges where the reality of sexual issues is ignored and where both the student and the environment seem to say, "It doesn't happen here." Similarly, parents may contribute unwittingly to such reinforcement by avoiding frank discussion of these issues and by handing their adolescent children over to a college in the expectation that the college will teach them; or by denying the question entirely on the assumption that it will take care of itself.

Contraceptives may also be rejected when one or both partners feel that the woman or the act itself is thereby debased. They may feel, without fully appreciating the lifelong consequences of pregnancy, that honor or morality requires them to risk it. Here, too, we see the effect of a kind of rigid and literal, late adolescent idealism that can result in irresponsible action. Other less conscious issues may be involved in the failure to use contraceptives effectively.

Out-of-Wedlock Pregnancy

It is difficult to determine whether the incidence of pregnancy among unmarried college students is proportionately greater now than it was 25 years ago. Although some observers and investigators feel that there has been little change, it is possible that virginity is less esteemed by college students today than it was by their parents. Those who feel there has been an increase in pregnancies in unmarried students point to the often quoted but uncertain figures documenting a higher illegitimacy rate, the large number of illegal abortions, and the many marriages that take place after the bride is pregnant. Whatever the incidence may be, most colleges find pregnancy to be a constantly recurring problem in spite of the wide availability of contraceptive techniques.

The reasons for pregnancy occurring out-of-wedlock are complex. A small minority are genuine accidents—failure of contraception with the best techniques. Most pregnancies in college are determined by the concurrence of several causal factors: the conscious and unconscious meaning of the pregnancy for the couple, particularly the girl; the state of her mind and emotions at the time conception occurs; the character of her relationship with the boy; the nature of the life situation in which they find themselves; and the individual modes of expression of wishes and defensive patterns. A girl is more likely to expose herself to pregnancy if she generally tends to live out unconscious wishes in an impulsive manner. Given strong underlying wishes for a baby, the likelihood of a pregnancy is further increased if she has a tendency to avoid reality when under pressure from either inner feelings or outer circumstances. Of course, pregnancy has served since time immemorial as a way to get the man, and frequently still does.

The boy who carries out sexual intercourse without contraception also is likely to be expressing one or more of a variety of unconscious attitudes. He may be unsure of his masculinity and feel unconsciously that fathering a child will prove his virility. He may be influenced by friends who say that a different and better sensual experience takes place in the absence of contraceptive devices.

Other influences that affect the boy may apply equally to the girl. Either partner may be simultaneously denying yet inviting impregnation; either may be trying to resolve underlying contradictory drives toward and away from sexual intercourse, toward and away from an ongoing commitment to one person, and toward or away from marriage. There may also be conscious or unconscious hostility toward the other partner or toward all members of the opposite sex. Either partner may go along with the other's preferences in the matter without inquiring into the reasons for it.

Case Example

Jane was a good student in high school, but she felt inferior to her younger, prettier, and brighter sister. She was the daughter of a rigid, demanding father, a lawyer who had worked up to a position of prominence and success in the community at the cost of having little time or warmth for his family. Her mother, a long-suffering and placating woman, was caught between her concern about the opinion of the neighbors on the one hand, and her hopes for her daughters on the other. Although Jane had some dates in high school, she was possessive and seductive to her younger sister's numerous boyfriends. She denied any feeling of resentment toward her sister.

Jane gradually became preoccupied with boys although she kept up her studies and other school activities and was accepted by an excellent college. Once there she became an enthusiastic beatnik, the more so because of her parents' protests. Her relationships with men became more intimate physically and yet more detached emotionally, and she became increasingly blasé. She shared her secrets with a roommate who was a good friend. Soon she was having intercourse frequently with several different men, but she felt disgusted and frustrated after each incident. This pattern continued for two years.

In her junior year she formed a close sexual relationship with Allan, two years younger, who attended a school in a different city, and who was formerly her sister's boyfriend. For the first time she felt that she was in love. During a happy summer, she fantasied marriage and a full, satisfying life with Allan. His parents opposed the relationship on the grounds that it would interfere with his schooling, and Allan himself became increasingly ambivalent.

One September afternoon just before the impending separation required by the start of the school year, they went window shopping together, strayed into a store to look at furniture, and found themselves looking at baby toys. They spent that night together. She used no contraceptive and realized the next month that she was pregnant.

Discussion

Jane's original pattern of promiscuous relationships reflected certain major problems. Her self-depreciating behavior was related to her failure to feel confident of her father's love and to her estrangement from her mother. These damaged relationships contributed to her lack of confidence in her femininity. Her promiscuity expressed not only an attempt to achieve closeness with a man, but also her low self-regard and her angry feelings toward men. She controlled the man, in a sense, by offering herself without love. These compulsive attempts to gain closeness always left her with an empty feeling because she habitually used sex to express hostility, and because through it she was seeking child-like closeness rather than adult mutuality and commitment.

Jane could not accept Allan's ambivalence. He was a man who had belonged to another woman and thus the relationship represented for her a triumph over both her sister and her mother, whose men she had longed to please and win in childhood. During the summer, her unconscious wishes for marriage and family found expression in intercourse without contraceptives. She was unable to come to terms with the reality that reminded her of earlier disappointment, and pregnancy was a neurotic solution. Neither Jane nor Allan was ignorant of contraceptives; they had used them successfully in the past, but on this occasion unconscious factors determined the action.

Summary

It is not uncommon for adolescents to ignore the possibility that pregnancy may occur from a particular sexual act, even though they may be fully aware of biological realities. Sometimes this is expressed as "taking a chance"; sometimes the girl will say, "I just never thought of it at the time," or "I didn't think it could happen to me," or "all my friends have so many affairs and none of them has ever gotten pregnant. I didn't think I would from just one time."

When a girl becomes pregnant, she usually has four choices: she can marry the father of the child; she can remain unmarried, carry the baby to term and keep it; she can carry the baby to term and give it up for adoption; or she can seek abortion, legal or illegal. While these choices do exist, most girls need counseling to consider them. It is not rare for students to insist that their choice is between suicide and abortion. This state of mind, if not expertly treated, can lead to impulsive action and a tragic failure to acknowledge and deal with the many important underlying feelings. The traditional resolution has been marriage;

today it remains a frequent choice, but abortion is more often the resolution than in the past. Another possible solution, rarely discussed explicitly in a society that puts a heavy premium on social sanction, is an automatically arranged marriage to be followed by divorce after the birth of the baby. Such a marriage has the single purpose of legalizing the baby and the mother's situation.

Out-of-wedlock pregnancy cannot fail to have some serious emotional impact particularly on the girl, however it is handled. Although in some situations it can be a maturing experience, it is one of those human dilemmas for which there is no satisfactory solution. A limited set of alternatives exists, and one hopes to arrive at the solution for each case that will allow for maximum personal growth. The potential for maturation is enhanced if the young woman can examine the emotional and social consequences of each of the alternatives and make her own choice among them. One alternative is marriage.

Marriage

"Shotgun" marriages probably occur much more frequently than is realized. For couples who have long gone steady, currently a common pattern, a pregnancy may only hasten a wedding that is already planned. Even in cases where the relationship has not been of such long duration, the partners can often adapt to the reality and make a workable marriage.

Although marriages precipitated by pregnancy may prove to be as successful as marriages in general, any marriage that begins under such conditions has particular difficulties to overcome. The couple has very little chance to develop their own pattern of living together or to deepen their relationship before the baby arrives to complicate it. Resentment against the intruder may create problems. While some adjustment must always be made when the first child is born, it may be more difficult in this situation and the development of both the child and the parents is hampered. Conscious or unconscious hostility against the marriage partner for interruption of plans, for career modifications, or for a forced commitment may be shifted onto the child by either parent or both. And, of course, an unsuitable marriage always has its own element of tragic waste.

The traditional expectation that the pregnant girl will want at all costs to marry does not necessarily hold today. Often the girl feels that the father of the child is not the man she would choose as her life companion were she to have free choice. She may choose abortion or adoption in preference to establishing on the basis of expediency a relationship that she believes is not right for her.

Carrying Pregnancy to Term

The few unmarried pregnant college women who decide to carry their babies to term usually then give them up for adoption. Social pressure makes it virtually impossible for a middle or upper class girl to do this without either temporarily changing her community or pretending to be married, although there are occasional exceptions. Even so, a sense of wrong-doing associated with the deception involved may well color the meaning of future pregnancies. The student must face the fact that she is going to feel guilt, sadness, and deprivation when she gives up the baby, particularly a first-born child, the one that really initiates her into biological motherhood. An apparently easy decision to give up the baby may actually represent a postponement of full acknowledgement of the girl's underlying feelings. An example is the girl who gives up her baby for adoption apparently without difficulty, but who, weeks later, becomes emotionally disturbed.

Abortion

There are no reliable data on the frequency of abortions among college girls. In most states, a legal abortion is difficult to obtain. Either on medical or psychiatric grounds the pregnancy usually must be shown to endanger the life of the mother, although in some states danger to the health of the mother is sufficient. Even a hospital with a liberal policy will not easily permit an abortion.

Young women able to function in college infrequently meet the stringent criteria for legal abortion. Three procedures, therefore, are possible: the frankly criminal procedure; an abortion performed in a hospital under good medical conditions but on dubious legal grounds; and an abortion in a foreign country where such intervention is legal. All three procedures have drawbacks. In the first instance, the dangers to physical health, and even to life, of abortion performed by persons of doubtful or unknown training under inadequate and unhygienic conditions are unquestionably greater than the dangers if the operation is performed under proper medical conditions; in addition, there are some slight legal risks. The second solution is extremely difficult to arrange and there are psychological as well as ethical complications. A legal foreign abortion is probably medically satisfactory, but the expense and arrangements involve handicaps.

For an unmarried girl, the destruction of the fetus is an overwhelming reality about which she may sooner or later become deeply concerned. Much has been written about the possible emotional effects of the furtive and sordid atmosphere in which illegal abortions are performed; in practice, we observe that the traumatic results of a legal abortion are not necessarily less severe than those of a criminal one. We suspect, in fact, that there may be more unresolved conflict in feelings when the abortion is legal, simply because this type of abortion is usually arranged for the student by someone else (parent, family doctor), while the young woman herself usually takes the active responsibility in arranging for criminal abortion. As a result, legal, or therapeutic, abortions may be performed in many cases where the wish for them is ambivalent and where they might not have been performed at all without the active involvement of others.

The urgency to do something quickly may cause the outsider managing the pregnancy to brush aside or ignore the girl's important conflicting emotions. She is more likely to have faced them if she has taken the responsibility for decision and arrangements upon herself. A girl may plan an abortion, possibly even insist upon it, but afterwards, she may nonetheless feel a great sense of hurt and loss and be deeply resentful of those who helped to bring about interruption of the pregnancy. Even the medically justified and well-intentioned recommendation for therapeutic abortion can have the unexpected result of confirming a girl's unconscious fears of being unworthy to bear a child.

Role of the College in Relation to
Pregnant Students and Their Parents

Most parents still play, or feel that they should play—in some cases quite properly—legal, financial, emotional, and directive roles in their daughters' lives. An unmarried student may want to conceal her pregnancy from her parents but financial necessity and the difficulty of making safe and practical arrangements may ultimately involve her family. Students often anticipate intense reactions from their parents, probably partly from a sense of guilt and partly because they view their own parents as nonsexual and therefore as incapable of understanding. Parents' reactions are often not as drastic as students expect, although the range of extreme reactions may include manipulative, overprotective, and destructive responses as well as acute feelings of failure, disappointment, anxiety, confusion, and shame. When a severe family crisis does develop, the exercise of constructive common sense and compassion becomes difficult if not impossible. Professional consultation may help the parents achieve an understanding broader than their initial rage, disappointment, or self-recriminations permit.

When the student health service becomes aware of a student's condition before her parents do, a complex situation develops. Whether or not the health service made the diagnosis (and diagnosis should be available and private), the health service is inhibited by the rules of medical confidentiality from informing the administration, the parents, or anyone else. The student may be urged to initiate discussion with college officers so that practical plans can be made for a leave of absence or, if it seems appropriate, to inform her parents. If she has access to help other than that of her parents and prefers to use it, her decision should be carefully considered. Some leeway must be allowed for individual medical judgment, of course. For example, if an immature or disturbed student is handling her situation in a manner clearly harmful to herself, the physician or psychiatrist may elect to inform a responsible person with the knowledge, even if over the objections, of the student, as might be required in other medical conditions where the life or basic health of the patient is at stake.

Separation of the elements of medical care from discipline is important. If the college considers pregnancy to be an offense and punishes it first by betrayal of confidence (to dean or parents or both) and later by administrative penalty, students will soon cease to consult with the college health service and will resort to other expedients that will not be supportive and that may in fact be dangerous.

In certain cases the student's own feeling about informing her parents may be closely related to the motivation for her pregnancy. She may have unconsciously wished to become pregnant precisely to provoke some reaction in her parents. Thus, the pregnancy loses its meaning unless the parents are to be involved. Her pregnancy and her decision to involve her family may express the same needs; for example, the need to express hostility, to be dependent on the parents again, to be taken care of by them, or to be rescued from more independence than she can handle or from a crisis in some other area of her life (e.g., academic difficulties).

Psychiatric consultation before she involves her parents may help the young woman to sort out what she realistically needs from them (help with finances, with plans for the baby, with arrangements for an abortion), from her psychological need to force them to recognize her hostility, provocativeness, defiance, or helplessness.

Summary

Once an unmarried student becomes pregnant, emotional difficulties cannot be avoided. The student herself, sometimes the parents, and even some college officials may have the illusion that if abortion or adoption can be arranged, the whole experience will be erased. Nothing could be further from the truth. The consequences in either case will be less disastrous if the girl is aware of her contradictory inner feelings and is allowed to reach her own decision, with all possible help offered. In the event of abortion, the trauma may be lessened if she is allowed to experience it as a real loss, even though she may have considered it a practical necessity. There are also preventive issues involved, for if unresolved feelings about giving up her baby, through either abortion or adoption, persist, there is a greater chance of repetition of the pregnancy.

Homosexual Behavior

Anyone familiar with the Kinsey Report and the theories of modern psychology will not be surprised at the occasional appearance of homosexual activity on campus. Homosexual relationships involve moral questions, the complicating issues of abnormality, emotional illness, and legality that all combine to produce varied and complex reactions among those concerned. College officials confronted with facts of homosexual behavior have sometimes sought refuge in the idea that the highly select and endowed nature of the college student population eliminated the possibility of such behavior. The reaction of students and faculty as well may range from confusion, disgust, derision, or anxiety to sympathy. Parents and public may suggest that the college allows such activity and demand punitive action. The fact remains, however, that homosexuality occurs frequently in the college age group; reactions to homosexual behavior are usually determined by the conscious and unconscious emotional response of the individuals most directly involved in the question, whether as participants, observers, or those charged with responsibility for administrative decisions.

Case Example

Mike and Jim, both seniors, were observed by Ted in the spring of their senior year practicing mutual masturbation in the shower on their dormitory floor. Ted felt revulsion, believed that they should be dismissed from college, and informed a faculty member. He interviewed Mike and Jim, who admitted that in their freshman year they had been involved in a homosexual relationship that was sporadically overt, but that they had broken off prior to the beginning of sophomore year. On the occasion reported, the action had been impulsive and had occurred following a final class banquet at which they both had been drinking heavily. The faculty member then discussed the episode with a colleague who was opposed to any administrative interference. They decided not to initiate any official action. The first teacher later indicated that his decision was based on the fact that the students were to graduate in a month. If the situation had occurred earlier in the year, he would have referred the incident to the dean or to the college psychiatrist.

Discussion

As the two young men represent their relationship, both had experienced a period of overt homosexuality as freshmen which both had apparently succeeded in giving up. Viewed from this perspective the episode might represent a return to behavior long discontinued, but reactivated by drinking, sentimentality for the past, or possibly by uncertainty about the future, all triggered by the impending graduation.

The faculty members avoided being caught up in Ted's punitive attitude, but they were also unaware of the possibility that Mike and Jim might have profited from confrontation that their homosexual behavior had been brought to public attention. Were they inviting punishment? Were they expressing some problems about graduation? It might have been helpful if the students had been asked to think about these questions. Ted's reaction was a common one, but it may have reflected a need, which he but dimly perceived, to talk with someone about homosexual concerns of his own.

Significance of the Term, Homosexuality

From the psychiatric viewpoint, homosexual behavior does not characterize any particular clinical diagnostic group. Homosexuality is manifested in many ways and occurs in relation to a variety of conditions, some far more significant than others. These may include mild neurotic problems, transient experiments as part of the process of growth, psychoses, or deep-seated and serious personality disturbances.

In normal childhood development, the sexual drive with its pleasure-seeking aim is directed at one time or another toward both parents, reflecting the bi-sexual base of man's sexual development. Two periods of special intensity of the sexual drive occur in relation to the rest of the personality; roughly between ages 4 and 6 and later commencing roughly between ages 11 and 14 and continuing into the second decade. It is important to recognize that these are normal phases of development and that individuals may experience sexual feelings toward someone of the same or opposite sex at different times on the way toward adult heterosexual choice. Viewed in this way, homosexuality in adult life constitutes a developmental arrest at a particular sexual level. Psychiatrists use the word *homosexual* to describe particular kinds of feelings and conscious or unconscious fantasy of sexual activity as well as overt behavior between members of the same sex. As with heterosexual fantasies, homosexual fantasies may express underlying wishes for closeness, nurturance, or fundamental anxieties about competition, self-depreciation, inadequacy, and a wide range of feelings that can be portrayed in bodily, sexual terms including sadistic, destructive elements of the aggressive sexual drive.

One problem in discussing homosexuality is the tendency to use the term as a label without recognizing the many different motivations and drives that may contribute to homosexual behavior by a given individual at a given time. Premature designation of an adolescent as homosexual may foreclose the possibility of exploration and understanding of the real nature of the problem by the authorities involved. As in any case where labeling takes the place of understanding, the underlying realities will not be met and dealt with. Although such a label is unlikely to convert a transitional period of self-doubt into a final identity, it will intensify the young person's anxieties.

Manifestations of Homosexuality

Manifestations of homosexual feelings during the period of young adulthood vary widely. The majority of adolescents will not engage in overt behavior, and many may not consciously recognize homosexual impulses. A significant number of young people will, however, experience conscious homosexual wishes, and some will participate in overt behavior of varying types and frequency. The latter may range from isolated early adolescent masturbatory encounters to a relatively fixed pattern of frequent activity. Others may engage in homosexual activity under particular circumstances—after drinking, or after rejection or failure in a heterosexual attempt. The ubiquitous nature of homosexual drives and the ultimately successful heterosexual adaptation of many students who reveal overt homosexual manifestations at some point in their adolescence or early adulthood make it difficult to define the boundary between serious psychopathology, transient aberrations, and normal adolescent development.

Discussion of homosexuality has increased in literature and in the popular press, but the personal airing of problems continues to be difficult for those confronting homosexual feelings for the first time. The individual student may worry about homosexuality without finding an opportunity to vent his anxieties; he may have been exposed to misinformation and partial truths that lead him to misinterpret his own feelings, and a homosexual encounter or a homosexually tinged friendship may come to have a distorted significance. Self-doubt may be initiated by the individual's feeling that he has failed to match some abstract ideal of masculinity; he then may interpret this failure as evidence of homosexuality.

Official Attitudes Toward Homosexuality

The college official does not usually encounter these problems unless they are brought directly to his attention. They may come through the report of students, through arrest by municipal police, or occasionally through a student's own request for help. In the social context of the college community, individual incidents of homosexuality may be viewed in different ways: as a psychiatric problem requiring treatment; as antisocial behavior requiring external control; as a transitional phenomenon of late adolescence not properly described as illness or as antisocial behavior; or as a mutant life pattern acceptable so long as it does not disrupt the college community.

The psychiatrist may contribute to clarifying the relative pertinence of one or all of these aspects in a given case. Although he may be asked for an opinion in a disciplinary case, it is more likely that the psychiatrist will be consulted professionally by a student who is inwardly troubled by his own feelings and behavior. His decision to seek help may be motivated by a number of considerations: a sense of acute personal distress, the degree of interference with his functioning, his own self-acceptance, concern about his future, and even by apparently unrelated symptoms that become evident during a discussion of homosexual problems.

Whether a student seeks treatment on his own, or is referred by a college official, the psychiatrist works within the medical principle of confidentiality. Respect for the individual's choice in relation to his homosexual behavior is essential here, as elsewhere, in any plans for treatment. An individual with an established and committed homosexual orientation may or may not wish to change. Where psychiatric treatment is actively sought by the individual, patterns embedded and deeply rooted in the personality have their best chance for significant modification through psychoanalysis or long-term, intensive psychotherapy. The outcome of this kind of treatment is uncertain; it also makes heavy demands on the individual's emotions and on his time. Treatment is affected by a host of practical considerations, including the feasibility of such treatment while the student remains in college. If the disorder interferes seriously with the student's academic work or the life of the community, and if long-term psychiatric treatment is not available at the college, a student may be advised to drop out in order to make arrangements for the appropriate psychiatric help.

On the other hand, significant modifications of less radical homosexual symptomatology are often achieved by shorter, less intensive forms of psychotherapy. There is a good chance of success through limited treatment for the late adolescent whose symptoms represent a transient phase of his development.

Female Homosexuality

Although the preceding section is addressed to the subject of male homosexuality, many of the considerations apply to female homosexuality as well. The psychosexual development of women generally is regarded as more complicated and less well understood than that of men. The same is true of the complexities of female homosexuality.

Instances of homosexuality occur among women students probably as frequently as they do among men, particularly in residential colleges. Gradations of feeling between members of the same sex range from affection and admiration through idolization, crushes, and covert sexual responsiveness to outright sexual gratification. Social custom, however, tolerates public display of affection and tenderness between women to a far greater degree than between men. In contrast to men, women tend to express the intense emotional aspects of a homosexual relationship more frequently than the physical aspect. Even the physical aspect shades over into the accepted feminine role of tenderness, care, and nurturance with the result that female homosexuality may easily pass without full recognition by either the participants or others. Whether recognized or not, female homosexuality, like male homosexuality, has important components of exploitive, sadistic, masochistic, and other patterns of destructive or self-destructive behavior. Homosexual women appear to undergo more outward emotional distress, including despair, rejection, violent jealousy, and suicidal gestures, than do homosexual men.

Homosexuality in women, like other psychological manifestations, is not of simple origin and a single cause cannot be ascribed. Difficulties at any stage of psychosexual development may contribute to a homosexual orientation. For example, marked disturbances in the early relationship with her mother may lead a girl to depreciate the feminine role or to hunger in adolescence for a dependent childish relationship with a maternal woman. Similarly, severe problems in a girl's early relationship with her father may result in her feeling uncomfortable about closeness with men or in overestimating masculine qualities at the cost of her adult femininity.

An absent or emotionally inaccessible parent at crucial developmental periods without an adequate and fairly dependable substitute will result in difficulties in achieving normal sexual identity.

Case Example

Frances, a senior, consulted the college psychiatrist, stating that she was having difficulty with her studies. She said she was behind in several courses, had a number of unfinished papers, and found it increasingly difficult to concentrate. She also was frightened at the prospect of studying for examinations, feeling so unsure and tense and tired. She was a pale young woman whose eyeglases were rimmed in the color of her complexion. The beige, gray-brown tones of her clothing were unrelieved by cheerful colors. Gradually, she revealed a story of intense distress at what appeared to be the independence of her roommate upon whom she clearly was extremely dependent. Recently, this distress was reflected in general despondency, punctuated by espisodes of painful depression during which she felt utterly rejected. It was not clear whether the roommate was at all sadistically motivated in her independent activities and seeming unconcern. The depression appeared to account for the recent study problem.

After a few visits to the psychiatrist, Frances revealed that she and her roommate shared many articles of clothing, the same bed, and were sharing many life plans, including a summer European trip and a plan to live and work together in the same city following graduation. The roommate was described as a warm, vivid, extroverted girl, carefree and active. Frances said her father always had been remote, a "saintly" man who nonetheless had no personal warmth. She spoke more warmly of her mother, but she too had not been close during Frances's early years as the mother had participated vigorously in the father's busy career "helping others." As a child her anger toward her mother was expressed through a physical symptom. Frances recalled a family story that, as a small child, she frequently vomited on her mother's "going-to-the-city" clothes. No history of overt, physical homosexual behavior was obtained. While presenting this history she denied any conscious homosexual wishes or what she considered actual homosexual behavior.

Discussion

Homosexuality in women is deep-seated in origin, and its complexities are not well understood. Society's easier acceptance of some of the attributes of female than of male homosexuality reflects values placed by the culture on individual fulfillment; this emphasis is heightened by the emancipation of women and may obscure female homosexual behavior entirely or provide a rationalization for ignoring it.

On residential campuses, especially, problems may arise when students have as their models accomplished, independent, sometimes unmarried, professional women members of the faculty. Faculty members become objects of intense admiration and idealization with resulting emotional attachments which can shade into the sexual area. The management of such a situation depends in large part on the teacher, and it is important that the special faculty-student relationship not be subverted by the unsatisfied emotional needs of the teacher.

One additional characteristic of female homosexuality in institutional settings occurs in consequence of disruptions in a homosexual relationship; the resulting emotional upsets affect other students strongly and can disturb large groups of girls, even a whole dormitory. Other students may identify themselves with one or the other of the pair, or become frightened of similar feelings in themselves. Therefore, a prompt, nonjudgmental approach to providing help for the two who are involved will also help contain the spread of distress among the other students.

Sexual Deviations

Exhibitionism, voyeurism, and transvestitism are deviant patterns of sexual behavior. Such behavior represents persisting childhood sexual interests in exposing, looking, and experimenting with opposite sex roles in play. Related kinds of behavior find some direct or symbolic expression in the foreplay of normal adults. However, when these childhood components of sexuality become in themselves the primary sources of sexual pleasure, they are regarded as sexual deviations. These patterns occur in individuals who are plagued by deep-seated uncertainty about their sexual identity and adequacy. They represent a serious disturbance in the capacity for sustained intimate relationships with other people. The following case provides an illustration of deviant behavior.

Case Example

Jack was a college senior who was reported to have exposed himself repeatedly to high school girls while sitting in his car. The police traced him through license plates and arrested him for exhibitionism. He admitted that his trousers were pulled down in order to masturbate and that he was excited by the sight of the girls, but denied that he had intentionally exhibited himself, stating that he thought the side of the car prevented anyone from seeing him.

Discussion

As often happens in cases involving deviation, Jack's behavior came to the attention of the administration as a report of indecent public behavior. The public nature of his behavior and the fact that local police were involved required some sort of administrative recognition; its compulsiveness and deviancy required psychiatric evaluation.

Deviant sexual behavior is not confined to a distinct diagnostic group. It may be found in varying degrees of severity in a wide range of personalities. Persons with mild personality disturbances who become involved in transitory episodes of deviant behavior may respond well to short-term treatment. Compulsive deviant behavior is caused by numerous unconscious determinants that are not susceptible of change simply by the exercise of will. When deviant behavior has assumed this compulsive quality, the underlying pattern is unlikely to be permanently modified by short-term treatment. Straightforward administrative handling can contribute to the student's awareness of the reality, significance, and self-defeating consequences of his deviance. Awareness and acceptance of these facts can help the student to contain his behavior and to deal with his underlying anxieties in a constructive way. Although the student may not be prepared to accept long-range treatment, it offers the only realistic hope for genuine change.

Another type of behavior that includes elements of exhibitionism and voyeurism but that cannot be strictly defined as sexual deviation sometimes develops as a kind of fad on campuses. The exposure of buttocks or genitals to innocent bystanders as a kind of ribald prank or vulgar insult has provided many a lusty joke in the annals of literature and drama. College students today identify this activity as "shooting the moon," and a favored arena is public highways. One teen-ager protrudes the anatomical part in question from the car window to the hilarious gratification of his companions and the presumed shock of the unwary onlooker.

In evaluating deviant sexual behavior, the psychiatrist seeks the relationship of a specific symptom to the individual's underlying psychiatric difficulties. Student participation in "shooting the moon," panty raids, or similar group activities may involve exposure and may cause considerable social disruption, but they are not by themselves indicative of the individual phychopathology represented in solitary, repetitive, deviant sexual behavior.

Silent Problems

The range of sexual problems discussed so far has involved the overt expression of sexual activity. It is equally important to examine the meaning of sexual "silence" among another group of college students who apparently are not engaged in overt sexual behavior. The manifest presence or absence of sexual activity alone provides no indication of the meaning of sexuality in relation to the total personality. Thus, while the absence of sexual transgressions by a particular group of students may reassure the college authorities, the important issue psychologically has to do with understanding the basis on which sexual behavior is contained; i.e., what does the absence of sexual activity mean? Such silent patterns may range from students who have severely restricted personalities and for whom close contact with others is painful and frightening, to those students with more open personalities who are comfortable enough with their own sexuality to be able to delay sexual activity in a manner consistent with other important personality needs. These differences are illustrated by two examples.

Case Example

Frank was regarded by his teachers and peers as a paragon of virtue. A gifted student, he deplored the sexual preoccupations of his classmates at high school. He felt himself isolated but at the same time, he alienated others, his peers in particular. His principal human contacts were with teachers and the friends of his parents, all of whom were equally impressed with his seemingly mature attitudes. When he began college, he felt estranged and disconnected. He experienced academic difficulties and had particular trouble in the free use of his intellect at college where he was not able to succeed easily with the rote memorization that had served him well in high school. He presented no problem to college authorities until he made a serious suicide attempt that resulted in a recommendation that he leave school and seek psychiatric help.

In his work with the psychiatrist, Frank's exaggerated morality proved to be a desperate attempt to avoid recognition of his
envious feelings toward others who were more free in their
sexual lives. Marked anxieties about bodily functions and
pleasure made possible only the most tentative masturbatory
experiments in early adolescence. Because of his deeply dis-
approving feelings toward his own body, recourse to masturbation as a substitute for the satisfactions that were absent in
his personal relationships served only to increase his sense of
guilt. Unconciously he yearned for close contact with others
but he also feared it because of deep-seated feelings of distrust.
He could communicate with his peers only by a pattern of argu-
mentative behavior that had the ultimate effect of alienating
them.

Discussion

This student presented no socially destructive behavioral problems, and in fact went completely unnoticed, yet his constricted
sexual life reflected a severe general restriction in the maturation
of his personality. Rigidly controlled attitudes toward sexuality
were apparent also in his problems about the use of his intellect.
He was limited and fearful in experimenting with new ideas just
as he feared exposing himself in his interpersonal relationships.
Such students cause no trouble on campus since they are quiet,
self-contained, and do not come to the attention of college officials because of infraction of rules. Yet, their sexual silence
may represent as much of a potential problem as the student who
gets himself into difficulties because of overt sexual transgressions. If their learning difficulties are sufficiently severe, such
students come to official notice because of academic failure in
the face of adequate effort and fine potential.

On the other hand, the implication must not be drawn that
absence of overt sexual activity among college students is always
a sign of personality disturbance. Students may postpone sexual
activities during the college years while growth is occurring in

other areas of living. The student whose case history follows would not have come to the attention of a psychiatrist except that he was randomly selected for an interview as part of a research study involving freshman college students. He illustrates a type of "sexual silence" that has completely different implications from the previous case.

Case Example

In high school, Bill dated extensively and ultimately became involved in a steady dating relationship with one girl with whom he experimented sexually up to the point of heavy petting. This relationship came to feel burdensome to him and he finally broke it off while in high school. At college, he was interested not only in his assigned work but in bull sessions with his friends and in every opportunity for contact with new ways of thinking. He consciously avoided dating and he decided to postpone any new involvement with girls in favor of his academic work and what he termed "getting to know himself better." He conducted considerable and constructive re-examination of his values during his freshman year. He maintained friendships with a small group of classmates, limited his dating, and directed his energies mainly toward developing his own sense of individuality. In the interview, he said, "I am really concerned—concerned about developing myself—my own—what I am capable of—in finding my own happiness and finding out what I am, how I think, what principles I go on."

Discussion

Bill, like the student mentioned earlier, avoided sexual contact during at least part of his college life. Bill's choice, however, was conscious, purposeful, and consonant with his total development. His eschewing sexual activity during this part of his college experience does not reflect deep-seated repression, but illustrates a transient stage in his maturation as a self-governing person.

The presence or absence of sexual activity during the college years in and of itself gives little indication of the potential for personal maturation. As we have seen, similar behavior may result from very different underlying personality dynamics. In the cases cited, the element of choice was largely unavailable for the student who was compelled by forces outside his awareness into more and more restriction in his social and intellectual growth; his avoidance of sexual activity was but one manifestation of restriction in his over-all adaptation. The other student, in contrast, was able to exercise conscious freedom of choice in his control of his sexual activity and to concentrate on purposeful self-development in other areas. It might be noted here that a high degree of social and academic activity, interest, and success is not usually combined with a conspicuous lack of interest in sex.

Masturbation

Another type of behavior that shares some of the characteristics of silent problems is adolescent masturbation. It is not necessarily a clinical problem but can on occasion cause considerable anxiety and is best understood when viewed in the context of normal development. This does not mean that its practice does not cause many young people considerable anxiety.

Case Example

Henry, a sophomore, was referred to the college psychiatrist by his counselor after the two had discussed Henry's difficulties with his studies. He reported himself unable to concentrate and to "get down to work." Instead of reading his assignments, he found himself aimlessly leafing through pulp magazines, cheap novels, and the daily paper. He soon began to describe himself as lacking will-power. After considerable hesitation, obvious discomfort, and embarrassment, he revealed that he lacked will-power not only in his studies but also in controlling his, as he put it, tendency to indulge himself. Finally, he admitted that he masturbated from time to time. Henry hastily explained that of course he knew everyone masturbated, but he felt at his age that he should have outgrown the habit and that, even if it was all right to masturbate occasionally, he did it too much. He felt caught in a vicious circle. When unable to concentrate on his work he frequently felt the urge to masturbate, but if he gave in he felt depressed and even less able to work.

Discussion

The case suggests that even in our present and relatively informed era, masturbation may still represent a source of considerable conflict and discomfort. In the past, it was traditional to attribute various dire physical and emotional consequences to masturbation — brain damage, sterility, impotence, insanity, homosexuality. Although most of these frightening and extreme beliefs have disappeared, the severity of the taboo has not necessarily diminished. The intensity of feelings of guilt and shame has often only shifted onto other issues such as the frequency of masturbation, the persistence of the habit beyond a particular age, and the solitariness of the act. For some individuals this view will be directly reinforced by their religious beliefs and scruples. Henry's complaint of masturbating "too much" cannot be measured against any rational standard but rather expresses his feelings of guilt. In addition to concerns with the act of masturbation as such, an individual often experiences intense guilt and shame over the accompanying fantasies that he may consider unclean, sick, or perverted. For Henry, furthermore, the issue of masturbation was linked to the area of his academic work, in that there too he found willpower difficult when faced with the necessity to prepare tedious assignments.

Viewed developmentally, masturbation is a form of sexual expression almost universally practiced at one time or another, commonly starting in the first year of life. Masturbation does not depend upon full sexual maturation for its occurrence. From the moment at which orgasm with its intense, conscious pleasure first becomes experienced, it is an important issue. For a time it may represent the only form of direct sexual gratification available to a young person. It does not necessarily disappear once relationships with real sexual partners are established. Masturbation in adolescence varies greatly from one individual to another, and there is marked variation in the frequency and chronological periods during which it is practiced. Like other forms of sexual expression, masturbation serves, in addition to the discharge of sexual tension, a variety of purposes including different emotional needs at different stages of development for each person.

The physical act in adolescence is importantly linked with conscious and unconscious fantasy. Altogether, in addition to the simple discharge of sexual tension, masturbation serves such purposes as the reduction of anxiety, expression of hostility, fantasying of sexual experimentation, and assertion of sexual identity in anticipation or recall. Masturbation also represents a response to difficulties being experienced in personal relationships by providing not only pleasure but comfort and reassurance from one's own body.

Faculty-Student Relationships

College students frequently adopt faculty members as models or ideals. The faculty members assuredly are admired for their scholarship and learning, but emulation may extend beyond scholarship to the attitudes and patterns of behavior that students see, or think they see, in their professors. Emulation of other adults is another step in the progress from childhood's parental models to the relative autonomy of adult status. The relationship with faculty is often a potent force for the adolescent's growth and learning. The wise teacher can be aware of the student's many dilemmas and, for a brief period of time, may serve as a bridge between the more infantile attachment to par-

ents and the mature and more explicit sexual attachment to a
lifemate. However, complexities may develop in a teacher-
student relationship that is held together by mutual trust and
regard, precisely as a function of these qualities.

Case Example

Ann, a young woman student, conscientious and dedicated to
her studies, gradually comes to idolize her youthful English instructor, as a model of intelligence and as an ideal teacher.
Gradually, questions at the end of the class period lead to further discussions over coffee. The student is excited and stimu-
lated by the discussions and feels that she is fully partaking of
the college experience. These discussions in turn lead to a term
paper that needs to be discussed in the instructor's office. The
additional research planned quite naturally leads to repetition
of the conferences.

The instructor on his part is genuinely taken with the capa-
bility of the student and is conscientious in his efforts to clarify
her confusions when she asks questions after class. He is
anxious, however, to get some coffee before his next class, and
it follows naturally to suggest that she come along so that they
can finish the conversation. He is impressed with her perceptive-
ness and suggests the topic for her paper because he feels that
she will be able to handle it well. At some point, he finds himself enjoying the conversation on a level other than that of student and teacher. And, eventually, it occurs to him that perhaps
she is interested in him as a person as well as a professor.

Discussion

It is difficult to say at what point this student began to look
forward to the meetings with her instructor in terms of more
than specific enlightenment in her course, or more than intellectual pleasure. Education in the fullest sense means awakening and broadening in many aspects of the individual's outlook.
The teacher is expected to contribute to this in some measure in
addition to awakening, for example, a sensitivity to poetry. Be-

sides being an inspiring lecturer, this instructor turned out to be a fascinating individual—not at all, the student felt, like the male classmates she met at mixers, whom she saw as insensitive, dull, awkward, and crude, with the single objective, in her view, of "making out."

The situation as outlined may or may not lead to more overt sexual expression, and, if it does, a problem may or may not be created. The case as presented points up the possibility that an ordinary faculty-student relationship may subtly shade into a potentially overt sexual relationship without conscious intent on either side. The student, who is still in the process of emancipation from earlier dependent ties to her parents, quite understandably may be responsive to interest from an older non-parental figure. Her sexual inexperience, which inhibits her attachment to her peers, in a sense makes her particularly vulnerable to the non-sexual beginnings of the relationship with the instructor. The instructor, on the other hand, may be vulnerable to the unintentionally seductive admiration that the student is able to express about his real accomplishments, and he may have his own frustrations that make him susceptible to a more than intellectual relationship.

What will happen if the relationship becomes overtly sexual? If the teacher is single, marriage is a possible outcome. The success of a marriage begun under these circumstances will depend upon the capacities for adjustment usually required by marriage, but the student-teacher situation may impose an additional hurdle, rooted in the girl's immaturity and continuing ties to her parents. Immature attitudes, if unresolved, make the necessary adjustments of marriage difficult to attain. If the faculty member is married, the situation is obviously more complex, with little chance of resolution without considerable distress.

If such a relationship has unfortunate consequences, the blame will be attributed largely to the faculty member as the older and, presumably, wiser participant. This judgment will probably be made no matter how aggressively or seductively the student may in fact have acted. The action the college will take against either participant will depend on many factors, some more relevant and laudable than others. In one instance, a faculty member became involved with a student over the summer vacation. Although the student did not return to college in the fall, the liaison continued. Despite the fact that she was no longer under college jurisdiction, when the relationship drew public attention, the ensuing uproar resulted in dismissal of the professor.

It would be equally possible for a homosexual liaison to develop by the same general steps. A case history of a student who became homosexually involved with her teacher will illustrate the nature of the problem.

Case Example

The professor was prim, proper, moral, knew right from wrong, and could tell when a student was kidding her or trying to fake in a quiz or on a paper. Clad in tweed suits and low-heeled shoes, she was a lonely, severe woman who exacted intellectual excellence from her students and from herself.

Alice, a freshman, feeling lost and frightened, arrived on campus from a distant part of the country. She came on scholarship and had been the brightest girl in her local high school. During the first few weeks, she had gone to mixers, attended parties in the dormitories, and had one date. She was shocked and scared when the boy had kissed her goodnight. She had clutched her pocketbook to avoid his hand, declined to dance because she feared his wanting to be familiar. She sensed the boy's eagerness and awkwardness, his preference for sex to conversation, and she responded with disgust. The mixers she first described as "slave markets"; then, she corrected herself and called them "cattle auctions" where each animal was carefully assessed by the buyer.

Frightened, she threw herself into her work and, as in the past, achieved some sense of worth from getting A's. She felt reassured and pleased with this indication of adult approval, and brought many questions to her professor after class. In this context, their friendship began. By the end of the second semester, she had been to the professor's house for supper. They talked until curfew about intellectual matters and about her family and its modest origins. The girl immersed herself in academic work and wasted no more time on dates. She began to consider graduate school and college teaching as a possible career.

At first, she was not bothered when a rush of pleasure was excited by the professor's smile, but as the attachment grew and deepened, she occasionally felt troubled and hesitant at the extent of her dependence. She found herself dressing for the professor, thinking about her, and altering and shaping her attitudes and values with her professor in mind. She no longer wore make-up and had bought a pair of sensible shoes. For Easter, she bought a tailored tweed suit. The skirt was an inch too long, her roommate told her. It was not until the summer that an overt sexual relationship with the professor began, when she stayed several days after the end of school to do some special work.

Discussion

The atmosphere at this particular college gives the superficial impression that life there is calm and controlled and that the college community's values and standards are held in common without conflict. This atmosphere tends to stifle questioning and combines with the rigid social regulations to create a heavily repressive climate. Under these conditions, although she wanted desperately to confide in someone, the freshman felt unable to. In the atmosphere of apparent maturity and morality, there was no one to whom she could admit that she had a problem. It is probable that the actual episode had its origins in unresolved childhood conflicts and might also have erupted at another type of institution. It is certain, however, that it was to a large extent the repressive environment that caused her sense of helplessness and isolation. Of course, a major issue in this case is the teacher's exploitation of the student's trust, but even this very serious complication would be more susceptible of resolution in an atmosphere that encourages spontaneous expression of feelings, freedom to question, and candid exchange of information.

Another illustration of faculty-student relationships involves a young teaching assistant who found himself attracted to a female graduate student and felt that she reciprocated his interest.

Case Example

> At a small party in the instructor's apartment, Betty, a Junior, became intoxicated and the teacher had intercourse with her after the party. He thought little more about it, and was surprised and very distressed to be summoned by the dean two days later. There he learned that the girl had gone to the dean, stating that she had been attacked and forced into relations when her inebriated state made it impossible for her to protest effectively. The teacher stated that he had in no way used force, and that he believed that the girl had been an active participant. The dean was somewhat sympathetic, but when the Chancellor was consulted, he decided that the involvement of a faculty member with a student made the situation untenable and that the teacher would have to leave the university. The teacher indignantly protested that he had been framed by the girl; his view was supported by several colleagues. The dean, although he did not basically disagree with the Chancellor's decision, thought that the student was not entirely innocent and felt that some action should be taken against her also.

Discussion

The case illustrates the difficulty in assessing isolated facts. For example, what explains the hostility of the girl in reporting the matter to the dean? Even though one accepts the principle of greater responsibility of the faculty member, one must acknowledge that in this case and the case of the girl and her young English instructor, distinctions between faculty and students become difficult to make. One might be tempted to say that the demands of their profession as teachers require that they not form sexual relationships with students. This is unquestionably true, of course, in the case of the professor who seduced her student into an exploitative homosexual relationship.

This and other cases suggest the question: What prevents more faculty-student relationships in college from becoming so sexualized that they interfere with educational goals? Professional attitude, self-awareness, and empathy for the students usually limit a professor's involvement. The student is protected by his strivings toward independence from adults, the separateness of his social age from that of the faculty, and his natural tendency to become more deeply involved with his peers.

Sex Education

American colleges for generations have provided courses in what purported to be sex education, usually required, usually for freshmen, usually euphemistically called "Hygiene." These courses explained the anatomy and physiology of reproduction, often avoiding explicit sexual references by using examples from the plant and animal worlds. They were, in general, too elementary for the level of the audience, and did not even attempt to deal with human sexual behavior, let alone with its emotional and ethical overtones. Today, colleges are offering courses in preparation for marriage or family relationships; while they still provide biological information, they emphasize increasingly the explicitly sexual aspects of marriage as well as its psychological and cultural components.

It is a well-recognized fact that students frequently display gaps in knowledge about sex that cannot be explained by lack of available information. As a consequence of emotional conflict, students with access to the full range of sexual information will often fail to master or to make use of it. Thus, the value of courses designed to provide the facts will be limited. On the other hand, there is evidence that some college students are considerably less knowledgeable than they appear to be, even about such elementary matters as the menstrual cycle and its relation to conception or the sexual functioning of the opposite sex. Frequently, the necessity for maintaining an air of sophistication inhibits questions and provokes supercilious attitudes, with the ultimate effect of undermining the course.

It must be recognized that it is difficult to give any but conventional views of sexual behavior in a college-sponsored presentation unless the institution is unusually open-minded and liberal. Not only parents and local citizens, but sometimes individual students, may protest for reasons connected with religion, or their own feelings, what they consider too frank an approach. On the other hand, students are likely to feel that a strictly conventional approach ignores the realities of life and that a course using this approach is irrelevant.

Despite these difficulties, it should be possible to arrange for useful sex instruction. The college can reasonably expect that a course will (1) give basic information under legitimate auspices; (2) open a dialogue with adults and other students on more than a bull-session basis; (3) identify and correct some misconceptions; and (4) contribute to clarifying the college's ethical and moral position on sexual issues. This is helpful for both students and administration. It cannot, however, be expected to (1) resolve conscious and unconscious sexual conflicts that cause misconceptions; (2) eradicate sexual problems from the campus; (3) substitute for thoughtful and candid discussion between faculty members and the individual students who ask them questions or approach them for help.

Recently, students on a number of campuses have sought to publish articles and reports on sexual matters. College authorities often are reluctant to have sexual issues discussed in ways that could come to public attention, such as reports in the campus paper, publication of surveys, and so on. Administratitve hesitancy may even extend to discouraging visiting lecturers on marriage or sex and classroom teaching that explicitly deals with those subjects. The problem of sex is thus made more complex by the injection of the issues of free speech and academic freedom.

3

COLLEGE POLICY, CAMPUS REGULATIONS, AND SEXUAL CONDUCT

Campus Regulations

The American residential college provides a setting where students and teachers come together to engage one another in the learning process, but it also exists as a self-contained social community. Its population consists of two distinct groups representing late adolescence on the one hand and adulthood on the other.

Government of the Residential College

Responsibility for governing our colleges is diffuse. The faculty traditionally asserts its prerogative in the areas of curriculum and intellectual matters, and students are generally accorded a measure of responsibility for extracurricular activities, though students have recently shown greater interest in the curricular area. The college administration serves as a bridge of communication between these two and also to the adjacent non-college community and the interested public at large. In addition, the administration interprets the institution to those bodies charged with ultimate governing responsibilities, Boards of Regents or Trustees, and in turn implements policies determined by them.

Whether private, religiously affiliated or land grant, American colleges have a heavily residential pattern, and a strong sense of social community accompanies the essential intellectual purpose. The residential community emphasis is peculiarly an

American phenomenon. The social aspects of the campus unit have engaged the colleges in questions that would be considered unrelated to academic life in Europe, for example, where universities developed as a spontaneous segregation of scholars. The earliest universities in this country were established to train the clergy, and the pattern of church-related colleges continues to play an important role to the present. Later, the land grant colleges were established as an extraordinary innovation to extend the opportunities of higher education under public aegis to all who sought it.

Observers both here and abroad have questioned the wisdom, and indeed the practicality, of intervention by the academic institution in the private life of the student. Compelling arguments can be made for non-intervention in a non-residential setting. The strongly social aspect of the residential college as it now exists presents a separate set of questions which we address in this section.

The social organization of our colleges reflects over the years the mores of society. Whether the governing bodies are private or public, the institutions and their officers are necessarily responsive to the fact that favor and support may be extended or withheld by legislatures, alumni, religious, philanthropic, or other groups. Special problems are posed in a time of social ferment and change that intensifies the potentiality for conflict and misunderstanding, and they are duly reflected in the local or national press.

The Issue of Privacy

Students continue to be faithful in fulfilling their time-honored role of searching for values, identifying their own mission, and engaging in sharp criticism of the inconsistencies which they perceive in the world around them. Today they consider privacy as one crucial issue. Increased communication about sexuality and an apparent change in standards of acceptable behavior bring into question the kinds of parietal rules that have long had the purpose of restricting student behavior without ever raising the specific issue of sexual conduct. Proponents of the *status quo* might well argue that sexual conduct is indeed a private matter; that it should be, but that it will cease to be when a public stand is taken. Yet from the student viewpoint, most institutions make an implicit stand, quite public enough to come to student notice, and students therefore find it necessary to exert pressure for discussion and explicit clarification.

At a personal level, less commonly articulated, a crucial part of the maturing process for the young person is to develop the capacity for establishing a meaningful relationship with a member of the opposite sex. This aspect of development leads to pressure for parietal rules that allow for privacy. While this concern may at times be sexually oriented, the real demand on campus is frequently for a natural and relaxed atmosphere that allows intimate communication and that may, but does not necessarily, bring physical intimacy. In pursuit of this demand, misinterpretations frequently occur and spark much of the heat in student-administration disagreement.

Some of the questions that beset college officers are: Has the college a responsibility for defining acceptable limits of behavior within its buildings and on its campus? Even if discreetly practiced? If so, how can the limits be enforced? To what extent should students themselves assume responsibility for determining their sexual conduct? To what extent can they? Assuming for the moment that some cooperative effort is indicated, how can necessary congruence of attitude between students and officials be achieved in order to arrive at rules that will be respected rather than flouted as unrealistic or hypocritical? Since standards of acceptable social behavior change over time, how does the administrator maintain communication with students, who usually represent a different generation? On a more philosophical plane, colleges encourage independence of thought, judgment, and intellectual initiative; can this attitude be reconciled with a judgmental stance in the area of sexual conduct and morals?

The Range of Official Attitudes

In their markedly different approaches to these questions, colleges reflect the wide range of attitudes held in the society at large toward student behavior. One survey of the current practices of colleges as described in the introductory statement indicates that the different ways of answering these questions and controlling student conduct are varying mixtures of a few ingredients. These include:

1. Published rules and regulations.
2. Rule enforcement and disciplinary action.
3. Student government insofar as it has rule-making and judiciary powers.
4. Climate of moral expectations as established through handbooks, orientation talks, and the more subtle methods of communicating the college's expectations and its degree of tolerance for deviations.

Rules and expectations on the one hand and the prevailing adolescent standards on the other combine to provide students with a basis for knowing what is acceptable to their peers and to the college. There may be an easy equilibrium between students and adult authority, or there may be an uneasy peace between the two.

Published rules vary between the extremes of detailed specifications covering every foreseeable situation and a simple formulation of general guidelines. Regulations that are specified in great detail exhibit a concern for the minutiae of behavior and frequently deal only with superficial aspects of behavior. For instance, a coeducational college defines a date in its handbook as "being in the presence of a boy for fifteen minutes." Detailed systems of discipline for lateness in returning to dormitories are characteristic of such colleges. A state university counts infractions by the minute and metes out punishment by the accumulation of minutes:

> For every minute that a student is late she will come in five minutes early on the Saturday following her infraction. . . . If a student should accumulate over 30 minutes throughout the semester, she will automatically receive a weekend campus consisting of Friday, Saturday, and Sunday nights on the weekend following the infraction which gave her 31 minutes or over. A student observing a room campus must be in her place of residence by 7:30 p. m. on the day of her campus. At no time after 7:30 may she receive callers, visit in her room or in other rooms, receive local telephone calls, or go to the lounge. If out of her room she must leave a note saying where she may be found in her residence. Her roommate may not entertain callers in their room on the night of the campus. A campus lasts until the following morning.

Examples of additions to cover newly arising or purely local situations are found among the rules of a small Midwestern denominational college:

> No person is to be carried bodily from the building (dormitory). Coeducating while sunbathing is not permitted.

It has been suggested that a detailed set of rules is almost mandatory in state universities because citizens and citizen-parents demand such assurance and have some power to influence the operation of the university.

At the other extreme are colleges that limit themselves to a minimum of specific rules and rely on general statements, such as those of a private university in the East:

> All students are expected to conduct themselves in a manner becoming scholars and gentlemen.
> Any undergraduate may be placed under discipline when, in the opinion of the Dean of the College or of the Dean of

Students, his attitude toward his university obligations has been unsatisfactory.

This approach avoids defining "university obligations" and "conduct becoming or unbecoming a gentleman" by assuming that students are aware of conventional standards of acceptable behavior. However, if students arc aware that standards of the past are no longer realistic, the standards may well need to be restated by appropriate authority in terms of present reality.

Some colleges employ both a general statement and an elaborate set of rules, thereby attempting to establish community morale through understanding while strictly guarding against misunderstanding. For example, the handbook of a Southern state university warns in bold face type against, "Behavior unbecoming a University of ——————— woman," but it also outlines offenses and punishments in great detail.

The existence of rules necessarily implies enforcement mechanisms. In colleges, the enforcement agents are usually of four types: (1) house mothers and proctors who have a direct obligation to enforce rules and report violations; (2) campus police and watchmen who have the same kind of obligation in more public areas; (3) deans and faculty, who are less involved in the reporting of violations but usually have direct responsibility for taking disciplinary actions when violations come to light; (4) student officers whose duties may include an obligation to report rules violations and who also may be represented on a committee that determines disciplinary action. The degree to which one of these groups will be central in the enforcement process varies from college to college.

The Issue of Rules Enforcement

Enforcement of rules may be rigid, as in instances where penalties are spelled out and automatically invoked. Most colleges with detailed rules report, however, that ways are found to take the individual situation into account in the administration of

rules. Exceptions are often made in special cases, or in view of
a first offense. In the most benevolent systems, written rules are
substantially *pro forma*, each case being treated on its merits.
The most rigid institutions notwithstanding, it is almost universally true that actual practice is more accurately perceived
by students on the campus than by the most detailed examination
of published rules by an outsider.

The university's approach to specific violations goes far toward establishing student understanding of the intentions of the
institution and its grasp of their needs. No set of rules can ever
cover the multitude of interpretations or the number of borderline or unusual incidents that occur. In these borderline incidents particularly, the real values and intentions of the administration become apparent. It is here that the student perceives the
degree of maturity really expected of him; he learns whether
or not he is being treated with respect, and whether or not his
integrity is assumed.

The official disciplinary agents of the college are charged with
decisions regarding rule enforcement, standards, and, to some
extent, public image. On the other hand, the counseling services
focus their attention on welfare and development of the individual student. Although the two viewpoints will clash at times,
a *modus operandi* is usually worked out. For example, at some
colleges, it is understood that a student who is in difficulty (perhaps he has gotten a girl pregnant) may obtain help from the
counseling service without fear of discipline or exposure. If the
offense becomes known to a disciplinary authority, however, that
authority may take action. Thus, the student lives in two worlds:
he may communicate with one while in effect joining a con-
spiracy of silence against the other. The relationship between
the authorities of these two worlds, the degree and nature of the
intercommunication or deliberate lack of it, becomes known to
the student body and is one of the measures that students use to
evaluate the college's true intentions. Many colleges believe as a

matter of sound educational policy that the student must face up to the consequences of his actions in the world of law and authority; at the same time, the college offers him help through counseling in a confidential climate.

The Student Role in Government

Some form of student government exists in every college studied, but the extent of its authority varies widely. In many colleges, it is substantially limited to the administration of student activities. In others, student courts and judicial committees handle infractions of social regulations within specified limits. It is doubtful that many student officers will have the balance and understanding needed to handle cases of sexual transgression among their peers. Cases involving sex impinge with too much emotional intensity on young people who may not have achieved resolution of the related issues in themselves. Furthermore, student governments function largely in the absence of forthright declarations by college authorities about sex on the campus, so that even if the student officers could comfortably handle issues of sexual transgression in their fellow students, they would have no explicit standards to guide them.

The kind of sexual climate found on the campus depends on many factors: size of the institution, whether it is a residential or a "commuter" college, whether or not it has a religious affiliation, whether or not it is co-educational, and so forth. The following comparison of two colleges illustrates the effects of some of these factors.

Comparison of Two Educational Institutions

As we have reported, colleges and universities have varying concepts of the proper role of an educational institution in regard to issues of morality and the appropriate extent of institutional responsibility for the non-academic life of students.

Interpretation of the role, *in loco parentis,* differs from college to college, and on every campus one of its most complex aspects is in the realm of sexual behavior. Most colleges in the United States, however, today regard some degree of such responsibility as part of their function. This view is in contrast to the usual attitude of the European university, where students are expected to attend classes but may live anywhere and in any way they wish, an attitude almost nonexistent in this country in other than commuter institutions.

College A

College A is a private, coeducational institution with some graduate students, located in a community on the periphery of a large city. Although the college population remains largely residential, increasing numbers of commuting students have been admitted recently. The college's attitude is consciously liberal and *laissez-faire.* Students have considerable freedom, and the college makes a purposeful attempt to treat each problem individually. College authorities exhibit some interest in the student's personal life but tend to regard sexual conduct as a private concern of the individual as long as it does not interfere with academic performance or openly infringe on the well-being of others.

By agreement between the administration and the student body, the rules relating to discipline are published in an informal handbook oriented toward new students. Dormitory regulations for men differ from those for women; both may have visitors of the opposite sex in their rooms but men have greater latitude in hours and times. Signing out and signing in is required only of women, though they may by-pass the publicity of the sign-out sheet by verbally informing a designated faculty member of their plans. Although the rules stipulate conditions for overnight and weekend permissions, student whereabouts are rarely checked. Seniors in good standing receive special late privileges.

Penalties are carefully spelled out. A certain amount of deviation from rules is tolerated and, as in most colleges, a great deal of sexual activity is possible within the letter of the law.

Out-of-wedlock pregnancy is not an automatic cause for dismissal. On the contrary, emphasis is placed on enabling the student to continue classes as long as possible; this may be considerably after the pregnancy is outwardly apparent. It is common knowledge that students arrange for abortions and that withdrawals from college occur because of pregnancy. Open discussion of sexual issues takes place, and the student newspaper has published articles about sexual behavior, homosexuality, pregnancy, and abortion.

The college recognizes that the degree of freedom allowed students leads sometimes to anxiety and even to disturbance. Some members of the administration view such risks as the necessary price of freedom. They believe that the welfare of the student is best served by considering him to be a responsible adult and treating him as such, whether his behavior warrants it or not. This attitude obviously minimizes rules and controls over living quarters and, ultimately, over sexual behavior.

Although there is a college rule prohibiting behavior that places students, or the institution, in an unfavorable light, College A's relationship to its constituency is less complex than that of a state university where citizen-parents and legislators constitute a pressure for conformity.

Administrative officers do not acknowledge that deviant sexual conduct such as homosexuality and perversion might occur at College A.

College B

College B is a small, residential, undergraduate institution for women, situated in a suburb of a large city. Its attitudes and atmosphere provide a contrast to College A.

The official college position does not acknowledge the existence of student sexual interest and activity to anywhere near the extent that these are recognized at College A. For example, when a group of College B seniors asked for contraceptive information, their request was received with shock by a college official and was viewed as "symptomatic of the sexual problems of modern life." The official took the position that to provide such information would imply sanction of premarital sexual relations and the separation of sex from love.

College B sometimes takes an explicitly moral position. Although many colleges without special residence facilities for married students permit enrollment of married students and no official stand is taken as to the proper time for marriage, College B does not allow students who marry to remain in residence. It takes the position that marriage should be postponed until a woman is able to establish her own home. It is possible that, given its inclination to ignore sexuality as part of life, College B views the sophistication of married students as harmful or disturbing to unmarried students.

College B's published rules are more restrictive than those of A. Dormitory curfew and sign-out regulations are more strictly enforced, and the off-campus whereabouts of students is frequently checked. Rules are explained largely on administrative grounds. For instance, the stated reason for sign-out regulations is the need to be able to find a student in case of emergency. The effect of such regulations in limiting opportunities for sexual activity is quite apparent to the students, but this intention is not acknowledged by the college authorities. Similarly, a rule prohibiting resident students from owning or driving cars on campus is explained on the basis of limited parking space and is further justified on the basis that the rule encourages students to participate in more activities on campus. Students, however, understand quite well that an important reason for the existence of the rule is to prohibit the greater freedom for sexual activity provided by a car.

These rules, together with the prohibition of liquor on campus, make it possible to discipline a student who may have been provocative on vaguely sexual grounds, by displacing the issue from her sexuality to rule breaking. This pattern is, of course, discernable in many, if not most, college communities. One student, who had been disturbingly seductive to a number of other students, was quickly suspended when liquor was found in her room—a punishment considerably more severe than that meted out to others guilty of the same offense.

At College B homosexuality is either handled with severity or ignored. A student who is known to be actively homosexual, but who fails to break a specific rule, may be asked to withdraw, but the policy is not consistently enforced. A pregnant student, on the other hand, is automatically asked to leave when authorities become aware of her condition. She may be readmitted later but is encouraged to return only after her classmates have graduated.

Discussion

It is clear that the two colleges have quite different approaches. College A has adopted a *laissez-faire* attitude that stresses the independence of the individual, encourages him to regulate his own non-academic behavior, and makes academic values paramount; College B places equal stress on academic values but takes a more restrictive attitude about sexual behavior and often acts as though sex did not exist. Neither approach, however, fully recognizes the developmental issues of adolescence. College A fails to recognize the need for the college to provide some external controls; and College B sees the student as needing *only* the experience of external controls in regulating sexuality. Each responds selectively to one facet of the adolescent. For students at College B, denial is not a solution to the complex problems that exist, and frequently it has the effect of inviting duplicity and secrecy on the one hand and resulting in unexpected eruptions of distressing sexual behavior on the other. Paradoxically, College A also involves a denial: that some individuals at this stage of development cannot handle the new, stimulating, and possibly threatening experiences that unregulated sexual exposure is likely to bring.

Although strict controls and regulations have the consequence of driving sex underground and encouraging surreptitious behavior, rules do provide a measure of control and support for the student who is struggling with unresolved sexual issues and new academic pressures. Candor and clarity on the part of the college may be useful to the inquiring and challenging student as a point of reference against which to test and form his own evolving attitudes and convictions. Rules may permit him to postpone resolution until he is developmentally further advanced. On the other hand, if a student feels that the adults in authority neither acknowledge the existence of sexual feelings and concerns nor find them acceptable, it becomes difficult for him to integrate his sexuality. On a repressive campus, a student who wants help with a sexual problem may feel unable to turn to any adult, and an opportunity to provide an educational experience in the broader sense is lost.

The attitudes of the institution and its expectations of the student have important implications. Included are the range of alternatives with which the college confronts him, the degree to which his previous values may be challenged, and the picture of himself that he is encouraged to evolve. The institutional stance may influence his sexual maturation in the narrower sense, but it will affect his ability to solve the broader developmental tasks of late adolescence and to accomplish the major purpose of his being at college: furthering his education.

Administrative Attitudes Toward Individual Cases

The foregoing section illustrates differences in general administrative attitudes on campus. What are some of the considerations involved in individual cases? The following examples have been chosen to illustrate individual and group behavior.

Case Example

When Mary, a moderately attractive but immature freshman, left for her Christmas vacation, she told her house mother that she probably would take a plane which would enable her to return to the dormitory on Sunday night or the following morning. On Sunday night when her mother called the dormitory long-distance to check on her arrival, she had not yet returned. At 7:30 Monday morning, her mother called again but Mary still had not returned. Mary arrived at the dormitory a few minutes later. She obviously had not expected her mother to call at all.

Mary's subsequent story was that she had been sick on the airplane Sunday afternoon and was very ill when it landed. Her boyfriend, Jim, a rather retiring, insecure freshman with whom she had been going steady, met her at the plane and, being concerned with her condition, took her to his small apartment so that she could rest. (Overcrowded dormitories had forced the University to house a few male freshmen in locally available apartments.) Mary said she felt too ill to inform her housemother. She said Jim had not consulted a doctor, but had given her a sleeping pill. When she awoke, still feeling ill, quite late Sunday night, she felt it was too late to go to the dormitory, so at Jim's urging, she spent the night while Jim slept on the divan.

The housemother reported the case to the Dean's office. It was quite clear that had Mary's mother not called unexpectedly, Mary might well have told the housemother that she had taken an early Monday morning plane.

Both Mary and Jim agreed on the details of their story. In addition, both kept insisting that they had done nothing wrong. They also insisted on describing the separateness of the divan from the bed, and in stating repeatedly that they were in love and were engaged to be married.

Discussion

What action should the dean take? Certainly there could be more than one approach to the problem. In the actual case the dean's attitude and subsequent action were influenced by his concern with the immaturity of these two students and with what he considered to be their irresponsible behavior. In addition, he was aware that the incident was common knowledge among the girls in the dormitory, and he anticipated that they would use his decisions to assess his attitude toward the integrity and maturity of them all. The character of the protestations of both Mary and Jim clearly indicated to the dean that their only concern was that of being accused of sexual immorality. Although he was reasonably convinced that their defensive attitude indicated sexual involvement, the dean believed it unwise to question the integrity of any student without absolute proof, not easily obtainable in this instance.

Also, he saw the opportunity for placing the responsibility for dealing with the sexual implications in the hands of the parents where he believed it more properly belonged. He therefore required that both students write their parents, explaining what had happened, and then bring the letters to him for verification and mailing. He also took the opportunity to counsel them about the premature adult responsibilities they had undertaken in staying together overnight. From the administrative viewpoint he considered that both students had acted irresponsibly in not informing the housemother of Mary's whereabouts, and after discussing this with them he set the requirement that Mary be in her dormitory nightly except Saturdays for one month. This was accepted by Mary and carried out satisfactorily. Mary and Jim continued to go steady and three years later, shortly after graduation, they were married.

Differing approaches to this incident could be expected in colleges with different philosophies and from deans with different attitudes. At a college that preferred not to act *in loco parentis*, the dean might have taken the position that the students had actually violated no campus rules since the boy lived off-campus and the girl had returned to her dormitory by the time she had originally stated. Therefore, after informing the girl's mother of her return, he might have left the matter entirely to the parents, inasmuch as it had primarily involved the relationship of the girl with her parents. At another college, the consideration of any infraction of sign-in rules, might have been referred to a student disciplinary board, thereby freeing the dean of some disciplinary problems and also setting in motion whatever gains might derive from learning among peers. In still another college that took the view that a student's life off-campus was a matter of his own private concern, the dean might not have considered the issue of sexual transgression at all. Yet another dean might have refrained from having letters brought to him to read and mail as he might have sensed a predictable antagonism that would interfere with the effectiveness of the counseling which he was attempting. He might have called Mary's mother and then written to Jim's parents himself. Disciplinary action for Jim might have been considered also. In still a different college where sexual involvement would be considered reason for expulsion, it might have been of primary concern to learn the exact truth about the sexual relationship. The expectation of setting an example for others would outweigh the concern about the possible damage to the couple involved.

The Institution "in loco parentis"

No matter which way this particular incident were handled, certain specific effects and reactions affecting both the individual students and the student body in general are predictable. It should be of primary concern for students to learn improved methods of social and personal adaptation from such incidents. When this purpose is accomplished, the total learning process at college will be enhanced; but failure on this score will almost certainly bring distractions, upheavals, and tensions that interfere seriously with basic educational goals.

The process of personal growth and development requires respect of privacy. The principle of *in loco parentis,* however, appears to be in direct conflict with the principle of privacy, and this is an important reason for the persistent, serious questioning of the institutional role as parent.

The conflict draws attention to what may be a fundamental flaw in the capacity of an institution to act as surrogate parent even in the presence of a strong sense of institutional responsibility. Parents have certain advantages that colleges lack: some consistent knowledge of their offspring over the entire course of his development; the flexibility of supporting privacy or intervening as the particulars of the situation indicate; and the essential privacy of the family role that may have to stand some test of public opinion, but that certainly is not subject to review by committees and press. This may suggest that the institutional role of acting *in loco parentis* is simply unworkable.

A second case involves group behavior and is more diffuse in focus:

Case Example
> On a warm spring night, just prior to the examination period, a group of freshmen massed in their residential quadrangle. After a certain amount of milling around, some of them began a movement to invade the women's dormitory. This was taken up enthusiastically, and the entire group marched to the women's dormitory. Their coming was heralded by their shouting, and the girls greeted the approach of the group with a shower of underclothes as well as considerable raillery. In the meantime, the campus police arrived and began attempting to disperse the group. In general, there was no real difficulty, but three of the group attempted to scale the fire escape and were apprehended by the police. These students were placed on probation.

Discussion
College campuses are often rocked by student riots and other instances of mass behavior. It is not clear whether such behavior is more likely to occur in non-coeducational settings; riots have recently occurred in both situations. Nor is it clear whether such behavior is basically an expression of sexual tension. The range of behavior is wide, varying from noisy milling around to outright violence and organized vandalism. The panty raid is a

traditional activity, and although this phenomenon presumably has sexual overtones, the real well-springs are difficult to ascertain. Even in an openly sexual incident of a group of male students having sexual relations with one girl, the motivation may be lodged less in sexual impulse than in a desire to belong to the group or in a fear of being considered lacking in masculinity.

Mass behavior of any sort is of concern to college authorities unless the occurrences are kept within reasonable bounds and without danger of personal injury or serious property damage. Some authorities believe that the energies and initiative represented in such outbursts, if channeled and utilized properly, are vital to the whole educational process. To the extent that these incidents are representative of a need or desire to express independence, it is important to recognize that severely repressive regulations may act as goads to rebellious behavior, and that some means must be found that allow expression of these drives for independence in nondestructive ways. Similarly, if the outbursts are related to undirected sexual energies, as they may well be, the authorities may attempt to encourage a social life to help satisfy these needs in a manner that will not overly distract student time or attention from the basic educational goals. It should also be recognized that successful resolution of such problems will enhance the possibilities of attaining the broad range of educational goals.

4

GUIDELINES FOR COLLEGE POLICY TOWARD SEXUALITY

In the preceding sections, many questions have been raised, and attempts have been made to place sexual development and behavior in perspective against the broader background of the college endeavor and the individual's striving for maturity. Some of the questions facing college officials were outlined. Discussion of these issues stressed that any action or policy may have different effects depending on the circumstances and the individual; a single ideal policy would be impossible to achieve. But the obvious question arises: in the light of psychological knowledge are there any general administrative attitudes that seem at least preferable, if not ideal? Are there any general principles that, if adopted, will have better results than others? We believe that there are such preferable policies and principles, and we have tried to incorporate them into some general guidelines with the hope that college officials may find them helpful.

General Guides

1. *Privacy*
The capacity for discretion constitutes an element of mature judgment. The student's privacy requires respect; sexual activity privately practiced with appropriate attention to the sensitivities of other people should not be the direct concern of the administration. Sexual activity that is not private is likely to be disturbing to others, and a student's failure to insure the privacy of his sexual life places it outside the private domain and

in the realm of public concern. In a dormitory situation, regulations are necessary to maintain order and to control behavior that impinges upon the freedom and privacy of other students. Rules may vary depending on the circumstances of the campus (coeducational, all-male, all-female, existence of adequate social halls, and so on). Ideally, the regulations will encourage informal contacts but maintain some measure of available external control so that students will feel neither burdened nor frightened by their freedom. Moreover, students want opportunities both to be in social groups and to be by themselves. Both needs should be recognized and provisions made for them.

2. *College Rules*

A sound rules structure will attempt to take into account the student who needs or seeks shelter as well as the more mature student whose development will require some elbow room for experimentation. Although this kind of structure is not simple to devise, it will benefit a range of students whose developmental needs vary. The student who finds rules useful as a protection or a limit will have some acceptable backing, and the student who feels less need for rules will have avenues open to establish greater independence. Many colleges employ a gradient of rules throughout the college experience that shifts to the student more and more responsibility for his own behavior and supports his expectations of himself as growing toward more autonomy. The developmental position of the 18-year-old freshman in transition from home to college is quite different from the position of the 21-year-old senior in transition from college to a wider world of experience. self-determined choices, and self-reliance.

One college included a statement by the American Civil Liberties Union as a guide in its policy on dormitory rules. We quote an excerpt here.

> Insofar as the institution is responsible for the welfare and guidance of its students, it can and must exercise reasonable

control over their scholastic life and much of their general activity. Not to do so would be to fail in the discharge of the educational function. But the school or college is also committed to daily, progressive withdrawal of its authority. . .

3. *Explicit Statements*

In the process of formulating policy it may be helpful for college officials to distinguish between rules that are designed to prevent sexual activity and rules that might make sexual activity possible while not intended as prescribing it. Further, it is desirable for the college to make explicit its attitude toward sex on the campus. The absence of direct confrontation on the sex issue invites students to disregard, interpret, misinterpret, and make what they will of campus regulations. Students may attempt to place responsibility for their own behavior in the hands of the administration by reading into regulations a confirmation or denial of their "right" to sexual freedom. In other words, if visiting in rooms is allowed and therefore makes sexual intercourse possible, students may interpret this to imply administrative approval. In the final analysis, the college cannot control the sexual behavior of students, but college officials can be clear and explicit about their own and the college's expectations of acceptable behavior on the campus. For example, if the institution disapproves of sexual intercourse in the dormitories and is not prepared to tolerate self-regulation of sexual behavior by students, it should be prepared to state explicitly that the college does not consider the dormitories an appropriate place for intercourse, that any students who had thought otherwise were mistaken, and that such activity will not be condoned.

It is not realistic for students to expect the administration necessarily to approve of their own private behavior. On the other hand, students would benefit in their attempt to make responsible choices on their own if the college were to make its own position clear.

No college officer needs to be reminded that incidents involving student sexual behavior often receive sensational publicity, although the degree of interest taken by the press may be unrelated to the seriousness of the act. Publicity inevitably complicates administrative processes. The action of the college in publicly known instances of sexual transgression will be carefully scrutinized, and may be questioned by trustees or by political or civic groups. If the situation involves individuals outside the college, or approaches the proportions of a scandal, it is reasonable to anticipate that the institution will be challenged to reveal and defend its policies and disciplinary procedures.

The interests of both the college and the students are best served if the administration is in a position to base its action on an appropriate and consistent set of principles and policies. In the face of strong emotion and its attendant pressures, clarity of judgment and carefully considered decisions assume special importance. These are more likely to be fostered when administrative review of a case can be undertaken in a framework of policy carefully and realistically developed in advance of crisis. This is not to say that policy should remain static or rigid. There will naturally be an ongoing process of discussion of the issues, and as new cases occur, they can be studied against the background of experience.

4. *Student Participation in Policy Development*

In developing policy, thoughtful consideration of the student viewpoint is realistic and will help to enlist student support. To avoid misunderstanding about the scope of student and administrative spheres of responsibility, it will be useful to make explicit the reality that while students' views are taken into account, ultimate responsibility for policy and resulting action remains in the hands of the administration. This principle also applies to disciplinary and judicial committees where student participation may also be desirable. Just as students cannot realistically expect that the administration will necessarily approve of their sexual conduct, so is it similarly unrealistic for the administration to expect that students will always approve of administrative policy.

5. *The Role of the Psychiatrist*

The specialized knowledge of the psychiatrist may be useful in developing policy and in assessing individual disciplinary cases. The psychiatrist's judgment is valuable in identifying those elements of severe emotional disorder that place a case beyond normal disciplinary considerations. In general, those situations that invite psychiatric consultation are major infractions, a pattern of repeated infractions, or infractions involving bizarre behavior. When disciplinary cases are referred for psychiatric evaluation, the student should be fully aware that in this instance a report will be made available to the administration. It is to be hoped that the consultation may make it possible for the administration's decision to be based upon the most complete knowledge available about the underlying nature of the individual problem. It is crucial at the same time to respect the confidentiality essential to a relationship providing this kind of information. Any breach will quickly reduce student trust in the campus psychiatrist and to this extent will render the administration less knowledgeable about the real nature of student problems. The psychiatrist can contribute additional perspective to the assessment of a disciplinary case, but the total evaluation, including the weighing of the psychiatric opinion, is, like the ultimate administrative decision, the function of the administrator.

Situations exist in which the psychiatrist finds it impossible to advise the administration; for example, when he has been seeing in treatment a student who becomes involved in a sexual transgression leading to possible administrative action. The major reason for the psychiatrist's inability to function as a consultant to the administration and, at the same time, continue as the student's psychotherapist is that the student's trust in the confidentiality of the psychotherapeutic relationship is a necessary condition for its effectiveness. Violation of confidence, even when it might appear to some as in the student's best interests, will interfere seriously with effective treatment. An alternative is for the psychiatric evaluation in relation to the disciplinary question to be made by another psychiatrist whose consultative function to the administration is made explicit to the student ahead of time. The psychotherapist can then continue his work with the student, helping him deal with whatever ensues as a consequence of the student's behavior, the other doctor's evaluation, and the administrative action.

The student who becomes involved in bizarre behavior or repeated sexual transgressions may suffer from an underlying emotional disorder indicating referral for psychiatric treatment. Disturbed behavior is frequently a way of communicating to others that a problem exists. Psychiatric referral should not, however, be limited to students exhibiting extremes of behavior; psychiatric consultation should also be available to students who encounter temporary difficulties as a part of normal development.

The psychiatrist's unique relationship with students puts him directly in touch with underlying emotional currents on the campus. While respecting the inviolability of individual confidence, he can often make a contribution to administrative discussion about policies affecting the institution as a whole.

6. *Enforcement*

On any campus everyone knows that some rules are broken without detection, but general observance of rules is more likely to occur when infractions are handled with respect for individual differences within a framework of explicit principles. Specific disciplinary actions are more likely to evoke a thoughtful, considered response from other students if they have confidence that college authorities will attempt to make fair and intelligent judgments.

Automatic penalties are therefore subject to question. Identical actions may arise out of completely different contexts or motivations. For example, a situation in which a student or a faculty member was exploiting other students and coercing essentially involuntary behavior would call for a different type of administrative action than a case involving two mutually responsible partners even though the actual behavior in question might be similar in the two instances.

For many individuals, particularly those going through phases of sexual experimentation, the experience of a confrontation with one's own behavior by a person in authority will act as a deterrent and may have an educational effect. Getting caught sometimes has the salutary effect of enabling the individual to recognize the meaning and consequences of what he has done, and therefore serves as a step toward recognizing and assuming responsibility for his own behavior.

7. *Heterosexual Behavior*

A certain amount of freedom in the area of student social and sexual interaction with the opposite sex is now taken for granted within limits of personal integrity and public decency. We believe it is in keeping with educational goals to stress the responsibility of the student in these matters. At the same time, we believe that changing sexual mores and new social realities require the college to be explicit about its views toward sexual conduct on the campus.

8. *Contraception*

Most campus health services make available to students information and medication for various physical conditions. The provision of contraceptive information or materials, however, is not usually considered to be within the scope of the university health service.

The broad, over-the-counter availability of contraceptive pills, diaphragms, condoms, and foams indicates the need for a re-examination of this position and suggests possible modification to the extent that information be made available through the health service. To those who might advocate dispensing contraceptive materials, we would say that this cannot be done routinely or casually. Prescription of contraceptive devices requires as much judgment as does any other medical decision. It should again be noted that many students will interpret the dispensation of contraceptive devices as sanction for their use.

We believe, however, that silence is not the only alternative to dispensing diaphragms and pills. Providing contraceptive *information* in the college setting seems to us tenable and appropriate, either on an individual basis in response to requests or in the context of sex education. It is also proper that such resources provide information about the public health aspects of venereal disease. A decision to dispense contraceptive information but not contraceptive devices would be consistent with respect for the autonomy of the student and would place the responsibility for the use of the information in his own hands.

9. *Pregnancy*

Out-of-wedlock pregnancy is the most serious consequence of pre-marital sexual relations; it is also one for which there often is no satisfactory resolution, especially among college students. Pregnancy may raise administrative, medical, and psychiatric issues, but the primary focus should be on the two individuals primarily involved; toward this end it is important that pregnancy be considered strictly in its personal and medical ramifications. Young men, as well as young women, need assistance in taking responsibility for the pregnancy and in planning realistically for its outcome. Confidential consultations with the health service should be available for this purpose; the health service should also be prepared to give the student assistance in making the diagnosis of pregnancy as early as possible in order to give the unmarried girl and her partner as much time as possible to consider alternative plans.

When pregnancy becomes apparent, the college official is concerned with the problems confronting the student herself and the problems that he believes her pregnancy will create in the college community. On a small, isolated campus, the presence of an unmarried, visibly pregnant girl may cause so much disturbance that it becomes difficult for her to remain on campus. On the other hand, in a large urban university a pregnancy may occasion little notice. The decision whether to continue at college while pregnant (whether the student is married or unmarried) is an important one, and psychiatric consultation may assist in assessing the problem. Many illegitimate pregnancies are symptomatic of emotional difficulties; since almost all of the possible outcomes may cause emotional upheaval, referral to the psychiatrist is in order.

10. *Abortion*

Abortion is a solution to out-of-wedlock pregnancy frequently sought by college students. They may view abortion as a realistic resolution of the situation or they may make the mistake, also common among their elders, of assuming that abortion erases the experience of having been pregnant. Abortion is illegal in the absence of grave medical risk to the mother's life or health, and colleges are not, therefore, in a position to recommend, aid, or abet this procedure. The college can, however, provide substantial help through a counseling program that makes possible discussion of the conscious and unconscious aspects of the problem. Realistic counseling may assist the student to clarify her choice; it may also enable her to adopt a course that initially had seemed impossible (such as telling her parents) and thus pave the way toward a more satisfactory resolution. The student may persist in her wish to interrupt the pregnancy, but if she does so, her decision can be made with realistic appraisal of the alternatives and recognition of the problems and consequences involved in her choice to the extent that she is able to be conscious of them.

11. *Homosexual Behavior and Deviations*

Private homosexual, like heterosexual, behavior need not become the direct concern of the administration. Indiscretion, however, places behavior beyond the domain of individual privacy. If a student initiates discussion of homosexual activity with a college official, the matter calls for counseling rather than discipline; the fact of drawing attention to his (or her) homosexuality usually constitutes a conscious or unconscious distress signal, and should normally result in referral to the psychiatrist for evaluation.

Public behavior is distinct from the accidental detection of discreet practice; and both situations are to be distinguished from the individual who is approached by a plain-clothes policeman and trapped into implying a desire for some sort of liaison. The basis for administrative action will be different in each case since it is essential that each case be considered in its own context.

Dismissal from the campus is sometimes proposed in cases of homosexuality on the grounds that the college will not properly exercise its responsibility for protecting other students if it allows an individual to remain who is known to engage in homosexual practices. A substantial question exists, however, as to whether people of college age can be led astray in the sense that a younger person might be. The homosexual side of any individual's development may be intensified during the college years, but there is no evidence that the presence *per se* of an actively homosexual individual on campus will necessarily increase the incidence of homosexuality. It is possible, for example, for an individual to be homosexually active off campus and have little impact on his or her fellow students, while another individual with no awareness of the homosexual implications of his behavior might evoke emotionally upsetting homosexual responses from other students. This is not to imply that there are no situations where suspension of a student or faculty member clearly is in the best interests of the college community, just as it might be in some instances of heterosexual behavior.

In most instances psychiatric consultation will be helpful in distinguishing between persons with mild or transient manifestations who are likely to be significantly helped by brief psychotherapy and persons with aberrations that have their base in seriously impaired development. If treatment is recommended, there still is no guarantee that the student will accept it. Treatment achieves little without the willing participation of the individual, and it should never be assumed that psychotherapy can be relied upon to prevent or even to alleviate future deviant behavior.

Sexual deviations call for similar considerations. However, the most common deviations (exhibitionism, voyeurism) are likely to evoke the greatest administrative concern, involving as they do the involuntary participation of other persons.

12. *Faculty-Student Relations*

The college teacher respects the fundamental educational purpose served by his unique emotional relationship with the student. At times, however, he may become the focus for the student's feelings of idealization or unwittingly find himself the subject of unresolved childhood attachments. As a professional person, he is aware of his responsibility in any relationship that develops as a result of his teaching position.

If a faculty-student relationship becomes a matter of administrative concern, the circumstances of the individual case will naturally require examination. Psychiatric help should be available to both student and teacher. This may be particularly indicated if one or both become aware that certain aspects of the relationship are interfering with continuing growth and maturation or with the primary educational purpose.

13. *Sex Education*

Colleges have differing attitudes about instruction in sexual matters, and no specific formulation of subject matter will fit the variety of moral and philosophical positions that our colleges reflect. Certain expectations can, however, be made of sex education courses. They should (1) provide factual information and a legitimate forum for its dissemination; (2) provide an opportunity for open, objective discussion of any and all sexual issues; (3) identify and correct some misconceptions; and (4) clarify the college position on questions of sexual conduct. At the same time it must be emphasized that sex education courses cannot resolve unconscious sexual conflicts in individual students or eliminate sexual problems from the campus. Furthermore, sex education will inevitably occur in many informal ways in relation to the development of the individual student. Formal courses are no substitute for an informed and empathic attitude on the part of faculty and administration. Whether in the form of formal instruction or of statements in a student handbook, the college should make its expectations about sexual conduct explicit and make clear its willingness to discuss its position with students. An important goal is to encourage a dialogue about the student's responsibility to himself and to others in the area of sexual activity within the framework of the expectations of the college.

Conclusion

In considering sex and the college student, we have been principally concerned with normal development and its ramification for the individual, his education, and the college community.

In addition, this report reflects our conviction that the broad concept of sexuality can be most meaningfully understood when it is related to the rest of personality development at the particular phase of the life cycle under consideration. This, in turn, must be seen in the context of earlier and subsequent biological and psychological development. Thus, a discussion of sexuality in college students is immediately related to the broader concerns of human development, with focus upon the transition of the late adolescent into the young adult.

The integration of the biological drive of sexuality as a vital force within the personality contributes to maturation through enhanced self-acceptance and freedom for learning through active curiosity, energetic exploration, and receptivity to new life experience. Maturity of personality enhances the freedom both actively to enjoy sexuality and to choose and bear abstinence when it is necessary.

In addition to the suggestions we have offered about possible relationships between the adult world and the late adolescent, we should like to stress in conclusion the constructive potentials that lie within this age group, juxtaposed as they are with essential frailties of the human condition. The characteristics of the adolescent have been classically described as follows:

> Adolescents are excessively egotistic, regarding themselves as the centre of the universe and the sole object of interest, and yet at no time in later life are they capable of so much self-sacrifice and devotion. They form the most passionate love relations, only to break them off as abruptly as they began them. On the one hand they throw themselves enthusiastically into the life of the community and, on the other, they have an overpowering longing for solitude. They oscillate between blind submission to some self-chosen leader and defiant rebellion against any and every authority. They are selfish and materially-minded

and at the same time full of lofty idealism. They are ascetic but will suddenly plunge into instinctual indulgence of the most primitive character. At times their behaviour to other people is rough and inconsiderate, yet they themselves are extremely touchy. Their moods veer between light-hearted optimism and the blackest pessimism. Sometimes they will work with indefatigable enthusiasm and at other times they are sluggish and apathetic.*

Above all, the healthy turmoil of adolescence is a natural and necessary step in development from the ways of childhood to the ways of the adult world. From adolescence the young person emerges with the particular abilities and capacities, limitations and idiosyncracies that he brings to his adult responsibilities of work and family, and as a member of the larger society.

---

* Freud, Anna: THE EGO AND THE MECHANISM OF DEFENSE, International Universities Press, New York, 1954, pp. 149-150.

APPENDICES

PSYCHOSEXUAL DEVELOPMENT FROM INFANCY
THROUGH ADOLESCENCE

Sex is a dynamic force in man's life, beginning with life itself. This force persists through the decades as a fundamental determinant of human activity, and its manifestations evolve with each phase of human development. This concept, as we have already stated, is central to the understanding of sexuality at each stage of the life cycle. This appendix has therefore been prepared for those readers who may be interested in a brief, chronological statement emphasizing biological aspects of psychosexual development.

Sexual development begins in infancy as the drives interact with the child's human environment. From birth certain bodily functions necessary to life also provide the infant with pleasure. These biological functions require the mother's care for the baby's well-being and are related to the erogenous zones (mouth, anus, genitals). Hence the infant begins to associate these early pleasures with his mother who, in turn, represents his external world. Feeding is one example. During the early feeding period, the mouth assumes special importance both as a source of pleasurable stimulation and as a means of relating to the mother and the external world.

Although the developmental steps of early childhood overlap, each is described in terms of the organ or mode of gratification most predominantly identified with that period of development. The terms oral, anal, and phallic refer to patterns of behavior closely related to one or another erogenous zone of the body and are used to describe the early developmental steps. Each stage supercedes its predecessor in relative importance, but the earlier steps continue to play a subordinate though significant role in activities having to do with gratification. Successful passage through one phase naturally leads to the next, while unsatisfied longings and incomplete development of capacities handicap transition and successful negotiation of subsequent phases. Underlying this developmental scheme is the biologically scheduled maturation of ever more differentiated capacities: sucking, biting, walking, talking, increasing motor skills, etc.

During embryonic development, the fetus in the womb has experienced a nearly frustration-free environment, almost perfectly adapted to its needs. This condition changes dramatically with the intense physical experience of birth. Thereafter, the baby no longer is physically one with the mother. It is assumed that at first the infant has no awareness of bottle or breast as an object separate from himself and that he views his mother also as an extension of himself. Gradually satisfaction and pleasure come to be experienced as part of the self, while pain and frustration are associated with the external world and outside forces. In this earliest period we see the prototype of man's dual tendency to reach outward to other persons and the world and to turn inward to the self, the tendency to embrace what is pleasurable and to reject what is painful.

The Infantile Period

Several factors combine very early to direct the infant toward his mother and toward the outside world. Hunger and pleasure together with innate physical reflexes (such as turning and clinging) direct the child's drive to his mother. Repeated early experiences with the satisfaction of hunger and of needs for warmth and closeness provide intense pleasure. The frustration of waiting for satisfaction results in efforts by the child to obtain gratification and to maintain equilibrium by turning to his own body. When the mother is not available thumb-sucking gratifies the wish to suck but not the need for food. This frustration in its turn enhances the value of the outside world as the source for physical satisfaction not available in fantasy. The repeated sequence of delay, frustration, and satisfaction contributes to the growing capacity of the infant to distinguish self from non-self, inner from outer reality. The utter helplessness of the infant followed by the long period of dependency characteristic of the human child further establishes the importance of relating to the outside for the satisfaction of needs. Thus biological drive, innate physical reflexes, the sequence of repeated gratification and disappointment, and dependency early combine to further the relationship of the infant to the environment.

The so-called period of infantile sexuality extends roughly through the fourth year. During the first, or oral, phase of this period lasting until the second year, the child's relationship with his mother centers around having his bodily needs taken care of; this is represented most vitally in feeding. Feeding is important for the child's nurturance and pleasure, and for contacting and exploring his environment. He investigates the things around him by putting them in his mouth, by sucking, eating, and biting. Things are in fact destroyed by being taken in, but the infant fantasies that he preserves them by making them part of himself. The child's relationship with his mother is one-sided—she is perceived in relation to her caretaking function as the person who exists solely to provide satisfaction for the child. There is as yet no capacity for a relationship of mutuality— only incorporation.

Although the sexual drive in infancy is manifest pre-eminently in the wish to suck and the wish for warm skin contact, some genital excitement can be inferred from the presence of erections in male infants during this period. The origins of imagination can also be hypothesized as early as the nursing period as the child attempts to satisfy himself while waiting by picturing bottle or breast or his mother's smile. Soon these gratifying images are enhanced by the acquisition of memory and the capacity to differentiate between the reality of food and the pleasure of sucking and fantasy. The elements of external reality are also differentiated; bottle and mother as distinct from fingers, toes, genitals, and self. As with adult imaginings, the child gradually uses thought for pleasurable anticipation and for record keeping and reality appraisal in his beginning attempts to find satisfaction from the environment.

As the small child develops, he finds pleasure in many bodily functions and through this process becomes progressively more aware of the physical attributes and capacities that he recognizes as uniquely his. He also becomes progressively more aware of the varying characteristics of his environment with its particular quality and blend of stimulation, satisfaction, and disappointment. The mother's pleasure in play and in caring for his bodily needs will have important consequences for later self-esteem and his capacity for taking pleasure in his bodily activities.

As biting anticipates the eruption of teeth and the weaning process, the child becomes more aggressive, develops increasingly reliable motor skills, and requires greater supervision as he explores the outer world. Although nearly helpless and dependent, he feels himself to be omnipotent; he is demanding and self-involved.

During the second and into the third year the child becomes more interested in muscular activity, in issues of control, and in his budding sense of autonomy. The interest and pleasure that were earlier centered around oral functions shift to excretory functions. Oral activities continue, indeed thumb sucking may persist. Things now not only go into the mouth but are grasped and held, thrown away, torn, and crushed. Muscular development and coordination have grown apace and the child kicks as well as bites. Games of giving and taking are absorbing. He holds back and eliminates. He takes great joy in (or rebels at) his mother's pleasure at the first movement in the toilet. Yes alternates with No. This mode of relating to his mother is described as ambivalent. He loves and he hates. Through these years, the genitals play relatively little role in the child's pleasure-seeking activities; this period is known as pregenital.

The Oedipal Period (Ages 4-6)

The years roughly from four through six witness marked intensification of the sexual drive that will be re-experienced again at puberty. The genitals now supercede other organs as the main source of bodily pleasure and this phase is described as phallic. Masturbation observed earlier in infancy is now more frequent and sustained. It differs from previous autoerotic activities in that it is accompanied by specific sexual fantasies derived from the child's intense desires toward his parents, conflicts, curiosity about the sexual activities of his parents, curiosity about the difference between the sexes, and theories as to his origins and method of birth. This early intellectual activity is closely associated with the intensification of sexual drive and anticipates educability and creativity.

Sigmund Freud introduced the term oedipus complex and described in detail how the boy at this age turns to his mother with intensified love, wanting her as a sexual object, and hating his father as a rival and anticipating retaliation from him. Since he also loves his father, a conflict is engendered. The situation is resolved as the boy identifies himself with his father and internalizes imagined prohibitions and punishments, which the child exaggerates because of guilt over his own intense and primitive feelings, fantasies, and wishes. Thus begins an inner sense of self-criticism and an ideal, modeled after the father's attributes (as idealized by the four-year-old). The variations of the oedipal situation are many, but the specific form of the love and hate relationships and the individual manner and quality of resolution forecast much of the underlying nature of the psychosexual development that will take place at puberty. Until the oedipal period, the girl, like the boy, has been dependent on and has identified herself largely with her mother. She now turns toward her father for love, wishing to take her mother's place, and hating her. Resolution requires that the girl not only relinquish her father as the boy his mother, but that she then return to a feminine identification of herself with her mother. The threat of repetition of this regression to an infantile position of dependency, reinforced by the sexual drive at puberty, contributes to the girl's need to separate from her mother in early adolescence.

The Latency Period (Ages 7-11)

In the sexual pleasures of the small child, we see the forerunner of the progression and panoply of sexuality that bursts upon the individual at puberty. Although there is great individual variation, a relatively orderly developmental march can be described throughout childhood.

With the necessary giving up of his first love at about age six, the child has become dramatically more autonomous and now has a beginning conscience. The ages 7-11 are characterized by a period of relatively decreased intensity of the biological drive and hence are referred to as latency. Relieved from the internal stress and conflict occasioned by the severe internal pressure of the drives, the latency child busies himself with learning about the outer world. The vivid fantasy life and creativity of the earlier years is replaced by fact-finding, collecting, the acquisition of skills, memorization, and so forth. The child's conscience is primitive and relatively inflexible, based as it is upon an identification of himself with the idealized parents. The latency child's universe expands intellectually and through increased associations with peers and adults in school.

Prepuberty (Ages 11-13)

The period of relative peace between the developing childhood character and its biological drives is short-lived; indeed it may not in some cases be distinguishable at all. Prepuberty anticipates the onrush of intensified drive, for the second time at puberty. As the equilibrium of latency begins to give way, early evidence of the development of secondary sex characteristics may appear; cleanliness may revert to pleasure in being dirty, neatness to disorder, sociability to boorishness. Mood swings begin to be apparent, and rumblings of alienation from the parents may set in.

Adolescence*

Biological puberty, announced by the menarche in girls and by the capacity for ejaculation in boys and with development of the secondary sex characteristics in both, begins between the ages of 11 and 15 and represents biological maturity as defined by the capacity to propagate the species. With awareness of the schedule of childhood sexual development, we are prepared to see repeated and reenacted the various stages through which the growing child has progressed.

With the onrush of drive at puberty, not only does the genital component of the drive become paramount, but the entire range of infantile sexuality once more is reawakened. In this second edition,

---

* The Committee is indebted to Miss Anna Freud for her stimulating discussion with us of many of these issues. Several of her well-known contributions to the understanding of adolescence are listed in the Selected Readings.

however, the personality has changed and now assumes its own attitude toward gratification and denial as a result of previous learning from parental expectations, prohibitions, and rewards, reinforced by the culture. In short, what is known as character has been formed in many of its essentials in the years between 6 and 11. The personality struggles to maintain this achievement in the face of new impulses, wishes, and resulting tension. Those concerned with the adolescent may witness what seems to be the dissolution of the stability and quality of character achieved during latency. This impression is mitigated by understanding that this turmoil ushers in an intense period of growth: the transition from childhood dependency to the autonomy of the adult.

The balance of latency has been tentative because it depends upon an alliance between the demands of the child's conscience and other inner controls and a stable parental authority. This equilibrium is achieved at the price of sacrifice of pleasurable satisfaction of the sexual drive essential for adult sexuality and other achievements. Consequently, the upheaval of adolescence is necessary and indicates an effort at essential inner readjustments. In its absence, children retain the relatively amenable qualities of latency, compliance, closeness to parents, and childhood values and judgments in harmony with what they have taken over from their parents. Excessive early repudiation of the childhood forms of sexual pleasure may result in a crippling reluctance to grow up and inability to experience the turmoil of adolescence. Such comfort is achieved at the cost of healthy development of the capacity for full functioning—sexually, intellectually, and socially. In contrast are some outstanding individuals who seem to be continually adolescent but who possess as well a freshness of curiosity and a zest of life and intellect; who are also idealistic, artistic, and productive—qualities associated with the highest human aspirations.

In relation to the thrust of biological drive during early adolescence, the personality for the second time experiences the sexual intensity that characterized the oedipal period, but this time with relatively mature biological capacity. Again, the young person is drawn to the parent of the opposite sex, with an accompanying revival of the childhood wishes that had been relinquished or held in abeyance during latency. The revival of earlier childhood sexual impulses (pregenital) are associated with the ambivalence of the anal period or the oral aggression of infancy. The thrust of these resuscitated childhood feelings now encounters the value judgments of the conscience of the 12-year-old, developed in the latency years (7-11), and may assault the idealized image of self to which the young person aspires. This leads to flight from sexual feelings and from the persons (parents) to whom these feelings have been or are directed and whom the adolescent now may experience as causing the feelings and, therefore, as seductive. This can result in backing off from all adults or even from all sensuous gratification. Such adolescents may feel intense loneliness, sadness, or even grief at what amounts to the loss of loved, idealized parents. The intense self-involvement of this age period also reflects the fear and intolerance of closeness with the parents. Revived infantile sexual feelings may cause discomfort in relation to other adolescents as well, because of the associated primitive, homosexual, or hostile feelings. Masturbation may be the only means of sexual expression that seems safe. It is now accompanied by a variety of fantasies that will reflect the individual's particular adaptation at this stage; infantile, uncertain, hostile, homosexual, and adolescent experimental fantasies may exist along with relatively adult imagining of intercourse.

Within adolescence, certain characteristics separate early, middle, and late adolescence. Early adolescence includes the characteristic turmoil associated with the often dramatic physical changes. Rapid mood swings, regression with reappearance of early childhood behavior and dependency, angry rebellion against parents and adults generally, and a tendency to be with members of the same sex are all in evidence at this time. By late adolescence, more comfortable distance from parents is the rule, with more acceptance of the young person's own inner life. Already, the transition toward an adult way of life is noticeable with a shift to opposite sex relationships, more interest in sexual intercourse than in prolonged foreplay; some progress is noticeable in the selection of career and marriage choices. Rebellion against parents has lost some of its intensity, and signs of a friendly but autonomous attitude will be evident.

Perhaps we make the error of thinking of young men and women at college as children away at school or the converse of considering the college campus an adult community. Any college campus will include some slowly developing individuals still emotionally in early adolescence as well as precociously adult individuals capable of adult choice of career and marriage. The vast majority, however, are living out a period when final commitments are not yet required but are in the air. The psychological aspects of adolescence normally last well into the twenties, although biological puberty may appear to be completed several years earlier. Some individuals never really emerge from an adolescent adjustment, just as some individuals never progress beyond the characteristic adaptation of latency. Vestiges of adolescence may remain indefinitely, but for most the transition will be complete by the mid- or late-twenties, as matters of vocation, marriage, and identity are gradually settled.

B
SELECTED READINGS

The following bibliography is selected from a vast literature. Special attention has been given to publications dealing with sex in college. No attempt at a comprehensive survey is intended, but the items included are representative and many have extensive bibliographies.

Contemporary Behavior and Attitudes

Ehrmann, Winston W.: PREMARITAL DATING BEHAVIOR, Henry Holt & Co., Inc., New York, 1959, 316 p. (Paperback: Bantam S 2149)
A careful sociological survey of the behavior and attitudes of male and female college students.

The following three studies report the work of Kinsey and his associates:

Gebhard, Paul H.: Pomeroy, W. B.; Martin, C. E.; and Christensen, C. V.: PREGNANCY, BIRTH AND ABORTION, Harper-Hoeber, New York, 1958, 282 p.

Kinsey, Alfred C.; Pomeroy, W. B.; Martin, C. E.; and Gebhard, P. H.: SEXUAL BEHAVIOR IN THE HUMAN FEMALE, W. B. Saunders Co., Philadelphia, 1953, 842 p.

———— Pomeroy, W. B.; and Wilson, C. E.: SEXUAL BEHAVIOR IN THE HUMAN MALE, W. B. Saunders Co., Philadelphia, 1948, 804 p.

Kirkendall, Lester A.: PREMARITAL INTERCOURSE AND INTERPER-
SONAL RELATIONSHIPS, Julian Press, Inc., New York, 1961,
302 p.
An extensive study of college men; includes a comprehensive
bibliography.

Reiss, Ira L.: PREMARITAL SEXUAL STANDARDS IN AMERICA, The
Free Press of Glencoe, Ill., 1960, 286 p.
Not limited to college students; describes changes in sexual mores
and behavior.

Discussions of the Sexual Behavior of College Students

Cowan, Paul S.: "Harvard Parietal Rules: An Outspoken Appraisal,"
The Harvard Crimson, October 29, 1963.
A graduate student comments on the issues raised in *The Crimson* during the preceding month by students, deans, psychiatrists,
and others, for which see the issues of October 1, 9, and 11.

Farnsworth, Dana L.: "Sexual Morality and the Dilemma of the
Colleges," *American Journal of Orthopsychiatry*, Vol. 35, No. 4,
1965, pp. 676–681.
Advocates a middle ground between the individual and the
college.

Goldsen, Rose K.; Rosenberg, M.; Williams, R. M.; and Suchman,
E. A.: "Men and Women," in WHAT COLLEGE STUDENTS THINK,
D. Van Nostrand Co., Inc., Princeton, N.J., 1960, Chapter 4, pp.
81–96.
A sociological report of the views of men and women students
on dating, love and marriage, and premarital sex.

Jencks, Christopher: "Sex and the College Girl," a review of the
book with the same title by Gael Greene, *New Republic*, Vol.
150, No. 14, 1964, pp. 18–21.
This review raises the issue, among others, of whether there
should be more concern shown for those students who are
unable to achieve or tolerate personal intimacy.

SEX AND THE COLLEGE STUDENT

Levine, Milton I., and Pines, Maya: "Sex: The Problem Colleges Evade," College Scene Supplement, *Harper's Magazine*, October, 1961, pp. 129–132.
A plea for colleges to supply for their students factual and realistic education in sex behavior and attitudes.

Morgan, George P.: "Sex Behavior in the Modern Young Adult," *Journal of the American College Health Association*, Vol. 13, No. 2, 1964, pp. 179–186.
A college pastor discusses sexual behavior and broader issues of personal relationships.

Rule, John T.: "Must Colleges Police Sex?" *Atlantic Monthly*, Vol. 213, No. 4, 1964, pp. 55–58.
A former dean discusses the problem and some of its implications for the student and the college.

Sanford, Nevitt: "Morals on the Campus," *National Education Association Journal*, Vol. 54, No. 4, 1965, pp. 20–23.
Questions the presumed "revolution" in the sexual morality of youth; relates sexual behavior to personality development with implications for college administration.

"Student Sex Standards and Behavior: The Educator's Responsibility," *Journal of the National Association of Women Deans and Counselors*, Vol. 26, No. 2, 1963, entire issue.
Seven papers dealing with various aspects of the problem. Annotated bibliography, pp. 39–42.

General Discussions of Sex, Morality, and Social Policy

Cox, Harvey: "Evangelical Ethics and the Ideal Chastity," *Christianity and Crisis*, Vol. 24, No. 7, 1964, pp. 75–80.
A teacher of theology suggests that the current obsession with sex may some day subside and that the process would be furthered by a better understanding of reality and the Christian gospel.

Ehrmann, Winston W.: "Changing Sexual Mores," in Ginzberg, Eli, ed., VALUES AND IDEALS OF AMERICAN YOUTH, Columbia University Press, New York, 1961, Part I, pp. 53–70.
A review, with bibliography, covering broad areas of change in awareness, attitude, and behavior.

Heron, Alastair, ed.: TOWARDS A QUAKER VIEW OF SEX, Friends Home Service Committee, London, 1963, 75 p.
A discussion of issues and an attempt at formulation of a contemporary ethic.

Kirkendall, Lester A.: "Sex and Social Policy," Clinical Pediatrics, Vol. 3, No. 4, 1964, pp. 236–246.
A professor of family life reviews the many influences leading to the "sexual economy of abundance," points to many irrationalities in thinking about sex, and stresses the essentially social nature of sexual behavior.

Pilpel, Harriet F.: "Sex vs. The Law: A Study in Hypocrisy," Harper's Magazine, January, 1965, pp. 35–40.
A lawyer discusses the legal treatment of sexual problems and the irrationalities embodied in it.

Wolfenden, Sir John, Chairman: THE WOLFENDEN REPORT: REPORT OF THE COMMITTEE ON HOMOSEXUAL OFFENCES AND PROSTITUTION, Stein & Day, Inc., New York, 1963, 243 p.
A report including recommendations to the British Government. Not specifically addressed to the college-age period.

Psychoanalytic Studies

Blos, Peter: ON ADOLESCENCE, A PSYCHOANALYTIC INTERPRETATION, The Free Press of Glencoe, Inc., New York, 1962, 269 p.
Detailed description of development during adolescence, including the cultural and biological aspects. Extensive bibliography of the psychoanalytic literature, listing books and periodicals.

Brenner, Charles: AN ELEMENTARY TEXTBOOK OF PSYCHOANALYSIS, International Universities Press, Inc., New York, 1955, 219 p. (Paperback: A102 Anchor)
A clear, brief statement for the serious student.

Erikson, Erik H.: CHILDHOOD AND SOCIETY. W. W. Norton & Co., Inc., New York, 1950, 397 p. Rev., 2d ed., Norton paperback, 1963.
Concentrates on the interpersonal and cultural aspects of sexual development and aims at a theory of development that comprehends the entire life span.

———IDENTITY AND THE LIFE CYCLE, Psychological Issues, Vol. 1, No. 1, International Universities Press, Inc., New York, 1959, 171 p.
Three papers describing the growth and crises of personality.

Freud, Anna: THE EGO AND THE MECHANISM OF DEFENSE, International Universities Press, Inc., New York, 1946, 196 p.
The classical work on the ego's defensive operations. The last two chapters deal with adolescence specifically.

———"Adolescence," PSYCHOANALYTIC STUDY OF THE CHILD, Vol. 13, International Universities Press, Inc., New York, 1958, pp. 255–278.
A discussion of adolescence including psychoanalytic theory, clinical and treatment considerations, and comment on the concept of normality.

Freud, Sigmund: THREE ESSAYS ON SEXUALITY (1905), the Standard Edition of the Complete Psychological Works of Sigmund Freud, Vol. VII, pp. 125–245, The Hogarth Press and the Institute of Psychoanalysis, London, 1953. This edition includes a chronological bibliography of Freud's writings on sex.
Freud's basic statement of the growth and disturbances of the sexual instinct. The third essay deals specifically with adolescence.

Josselyn, Irene M.: THE ADOLESCENT AND HIS WORLD, Family Service Association of America, New York, 1952, 124 p.
A concise treatment of developmental issues of adolescence written primarily for psychotherapists, Chapter X discusses sex education and behavior.

Spiegel, Leo A.: "A Review of Contributions to a Psychoanalytic Theory of Adolescence," PSYCHOANALYTIC STUDY OF THE CHILD, Vol. VI, International Universities Press, Inc., New York, 1951, pp. 375–393.
Abstracts and classifies a wide variety of contributions; extensive bibliography.

Acknowledgments

The program of the Group for the Advancement of Psychiatry, a nonprofit tax exempt organization, is made possible largely through the voluntary contributions and efforts of its members. For their financial assistance during the past fiscal year, in helping it to fulfill its aims, GAP is grateful to the following foundations and organizations:

Sponsors

      BING FUND
      CIBA CORPORATION
      THE DIVISION FUND
      FALK MEDICAL FUND
      GEIGY CHEMICAL CORPORATION
      GENERAL SERVICE FOUNDATION
      THE GRANT FOUNDATION
      HOFFMAN-LA ROCHE, INC.
      HOGG FOUNDATION
      WILLIAM S. MERRELL COMPANY
      GUSTAVUS & LOUISE PFEIFFER RESEARCH FOUNDATION
      SMITH KLINE & FRENCH FOUNDATION
      TEKTRONIX FOUNDATION
      UPJOHN COMPANY
      WALLACE LABORATORIES